STRATEGIES FOR SUCCESS
MATHEMATICS

Judith Andrews Green, Director
Oxford Hills Adult Community Education
South Paris, Maine

Susan D. McClanahan
Educational Consultant

Donna D. Amstutz
Special Advisor to the Series

STECK-VAUGHN ADULT EDUCATION ADVISORY COUNCIL

Donna D. Amstutz
Asst. Project Director
Northern Area Adult Education
  Service Center
Northern Illinois University
DeKalb, Illinois

Lonnie D. Farrell
Supervisor, Adult Special Programs
Los Angeles Unified School District
Los Angeles, California

Meredyth A. Leahy
Director of Continuing
Education, Cabrini College
Radnor, Pennsylvania

Roberta Pittman
Director, Adult Outreach Programs
  Department of Adult Education
Detroit Public Schools
Detroit, Michigan

Don F. Seaman
Professor, Adult Education
College of Education
Texas A&M University
College Station, Texas

Jane B. Sellen
Supervisor, Adult Education
Western Iowa Tech
  Community College
Sioux City, Iowa

Elaine Shelton
Consultant, Competency-Based
  Adult Education
Austin, Texas

Bobbie L. Walden
Coordinator, Community Education
Alabama Department of Education
Montgomery, Alabama

STECK-VAUGHN
COMPANY
A subsidiary of National Education Corporation

Product Design and Development: McClanahan & Company

Project Director: Larry Anger

Cover and Design: Ellen Rongstad

Production: Carreiro Design

Editor: Enid Nagel

Photo Research: Carrie Croton

Illustrations: Denise Mickalson

Photo Credits:

Cover: DeWys, Inc.; p. 9 E. Johnson, DeWys, Inc.; p. 12 Ken Lax; p. 13 Photo Researchers; p. 23 F. Siteman, Taurus Photos; p. 25 T. Stratford, Photo Researchers; p. 27 A. Glauberman, Photo Researchers; p. 30 J. Munroe, Photo Researchers; p. 37 R. Borea, Art Resource; p. 44 W. McIntyre, Photo Researchers; p. 49 C. Cocaine, Photo Researchers; p. 50 M. Heron, Woodfin Camp & Assoc.; p. 54 R. Malloch, Magnum Photos; p. 65 Heron, Woodfin Camp & Assoc.; p. 67 D. O'Neill, Art Resource; p. 68 Ken Lax; p. 69 R. Laird, DeWys, Inc.; p. 76 Ken Lax; p. 77 L. Weinstein, Woodfin Camp & Assoc.; p. 79 A. Sacks, Art Resource; p. 80 L. Druskis, Art Resource; p. 81 W. McIntyre, Photo Researchers; p. 89 T. Stratford, Photo Researchers; p. 93 T. Stratford, Photo Researchers; p. 97 I. Berger, Woodfin Camp & Assoc.; p. 98 B. Kingsley, Photo Researchers; p. 99 R. Alexander, Photo Researchers; p. 105 J. LeJevne, Stock, Boston; p. 107 M. Heron, Woodfin Camp & Assoc.; p. 115 M. Uffer, Photo Researchers; p. 117 Photo Researchers.

ISBN 0-8114-1876-6

Acknowledgments

With thanks to Christopher Page for his contributions to the book.

And to Nancy Teas for editing the manuscript and writing the "Strategies for Success."

Contents

To The Student

THIS BOOK AND THE GED TEST

The five sections of the GED Test measure what you know about science, mathematics, social studies, reading, and writing. This book covers one of those five areas, MATHEMATICS. There are four other books like this one. They cover the four other areas of study for the GED Test.

The MATHEMATICS part of the GED Test covers addition, subtraction, multiplication, and division. It includes fractions, decimals, percent, and measurement. Like the problems in this book, most of the problems on the GED Test are word problems.

This book is a good place to begin preparing for the GED Test. It includes many of the kinds of problems the test will cover. And it gives you practice in taking tests.

STRATEGIES FOR SUCCESS

In each of the five books in the series, you will find sections called *Strategies for Success*. These sections in READING, SOCIAL STUDIES, and SCIENCE will help you increase your reading power. *Strategies for Success* in WRITING and MATHEMATICS will develop your critical thinking skills.

SELF-TESTS

Self-Tests follow each lesson. The Self-Tests are designed to help you find out what you have learned. The word problems on the Self-Tests are similar to those on the GED Test. They give you an idea of what the GED Test will be like.

ANSWERS AND SOLUTIONS

The answer keys at the end of each unit will give you the correct answer to each problem. The answer key will give the solution to each problem so you can see exactly how it should be solved. This makes it easier for you to see where you made a mistake if you got the problem wrong. And it will help you get a similar problem right the next time.

LEARNING HOW TO LEARN

There are tricks to learning and remembering. Try out different ways of learning things. Find out what ways are best for you. Here are some tips that will help you get the most out of any studying you do, or any test you take.

Keep a Notebook. Taking notes about what you are learning may be hard for you at first. You may think you can't do it, or that you can't spell. Don't worry about your spelling. Your notebook is your learning tool. No one has to see it but you. You'll be surprised how interesting it will be to reread your notes at a later time. And you'll be surprised at how much it will help you to remember. You'll find that taking notes is another way of learning.

Hard Words. It isn't necessary to know every word to understand what you're learning. When you come to a hard word, don't stop. Keep on reading. The rest of the sentence or paragraph will probably help you figure out what the word means. In fact, people learn most new words that way.

Understanding New Subjects. When anyone is learning about a new subject, understanding comes a little bit at a time.
It's like putting together the pieces of a puzzle. When you run into something that is very hard, it's better to keep reading to the end of the paragraph or section. You can put question marks with your pencil by the parts you don't understand.

Later, reread the parts that gave you trouble. Some of the hard parts will start to make sense. Try to connect the information you are reading to the examples or illustrations on the page. If you have a chance, talk over the hard parts with others. Don't think you have to understand everything the first time. It's OK to REREAD and to GO BACK AND TRY A PROBLEM AGAIN.

Use the Study Aids in Your Book. Pay attention to what the table of contents, the unit titles, and the chapter titles can tell you about what you're learning. The examples often illustrate the important concepts you're studying. Be sure to look at them carefully. All of these things will help you understand what you are learning.

Use the Practice Problems to Learn. Study the answers and solutions to each problem in the Self-Tests. If you get a problem wrong, this will help you understand what to do the next time.

Improve Your Test-Taking Skills. Many tests, including the GED Test, use multiple-choice questions. Each question is followed by five answers. You have to choose the CORRECT answer. Practice in taking tests like the ones in this book helps you to score higher on important tests like the GED.

Check What You Know

Check What You Know will give you an idea of the kind of work you will be doing in this book. It will give you an idea of your strengths in mathematics. And it will show you the math skills and problem-solving strategies you need to improve. These skills are important in passing tests like the GED Test.

Check What You Know is very similar to the MATHEMATICS part of the GED Test. There are 24 word problems on this test.

Read each problem carefully. Using the space on the page or another piece of paper, solve the problem. Then put an X next to the correct answer. There is no time limit.

1. Beverly and Dean both make deliveries for All Seasons Florist. Beverly drove 457 miles making deliveries one week. Dean drove 385 miles making deliveries that same week. How many more miles did Beverly drive than Dean?

    ____ (1) 72 miles

    ____ (2) 132 miles

    ____ (3) 172 miles

    ____ (4) 742 miles

    ____ (5) 842 miles

2. Three families shared the expense of renting a cabin on a nearby lake. The total cost to rent the cabin for June, July, August, and September was $1,800. How much did it cost each family each month?

    ____ (1) $125

    ____ (2) $150

    ____ (3) $275

    ____ (4) $600

    ____ (5) $675

3. Mike built shelves for his kitchen. He used $4\frac{1}{2}$ feet of lumber for each shelf. How many feet of lumber did he use to build 8 shelves?

    ____ (1) 24 ft

    ____ (2) 32 ft

    ____ (3) 36 ft

    ____ (4) 38 ft

    ____ (5) 72 ft

4. Melissa does gardening work for $6.50 an hour. How many hours did she work last week if her pay was $185.25?

    ____ (1) 23 hours

    ____ (2) 23.5 hours

    ____ (3) 27 hours

    ____ (4) 28.5 hours

    ____ (5) 30.5 hours

5. Richard bought a portable stereo which was normally priced at $79.50. It was on sale for 10% off. What is the total cost of the stereo including the 6% sales tax?

___ (1) $71.55

___ (2) $72.32

___ (3) $75.74

___ (4) $75.84

___ (5) $84.27

6. Carrie Martin runs Vacation Pet Care. On Saturday, she had 5 dogs to take care of. On Sunday, she had 3 more dogs to take care of. How many dogs did she have to take care of on Sunday?

___ (1) 2 dogs

___ (2) 3 dogs

___ (3) 4 dogs

___ (4) 6 dogs

___ (5) 8 dogs

7. In the course of a year, the manager of a car rental agency replaced the tires on all his rental cars. He bought 1,052 tires. How many rental cars does the agency have?

___ (1) 178 cars

___ (2) 203 cars

___ (3) 263 cars

___ (4) 363 cars

___ (5) 526 cars

8. An oil tanker held $8\frac{5}{8}$ million gallons of oil. At its first stop, it unloaded $4\frac{1}{6}$ million gallons. How many gallons were still on board after the first stop?

___ (1) $3\frac{1}{3}$ million gallons

___ (2) $3\frac{11}{24}$ million gallons

___ (3) $4\frac{1}{4}$ million gallons

___ (4) $4\frac{1}{3}$ million gallons

___ (5) $4\frac{11}{24}$ million gallons

9. Mrs. Lewis did her weekly shopping at the grocery store. Her bill came to $42.37. She gave the cashier two $20 bills and one $10 bill. How much change did she receive?

___ (1) $6.53

___ (2) $7.37

___ (3) $7.53

___ (4) $7.63

___ (5) $8.63

10. During a summer clearance sale, a department store offered 25% off on all swimsuits. Marta bought a swimsuit priced at $35.98 during the sale. How much money did she save by buying the swimsuit on sale? (Round to nearest cent.)

____ (1) $8.99

____ (2) $9.00

____ (3) $9.09

____ (4) $9.10

____ (5) $9.15

11. Frieda worked from 7:30 a.m. until 6:00 p.m. She is paid overtime for any time over eight hours a day. How many hours of overtime did she work?

____ (1) 2 hr 30 min

____ (2) 3 hr 30 min

____ (3) 4 hr 30 min

____ (4) 9 hr 30 min

____ (5) 10 hr 30 min

12. The Wongs had planned to use 500 gallons of gasoline on a trip across the country and back. They used 452 gallons of gasoline. How much less did they use than they had planned?

____ (1) 24 gallons

____ (2) 48 gallons

____ (3) 158 gallons

____ (4) 952 gallons

____ (5) 1,052 gallons

13. Mrs. Valdez does child care in her home. For snacks, each child eats two pieces of fruit a day. Last week, she had 5 children Monday through Friday. She also had 3 children who came on only 2 days. How much fruit did the children eat last week?

____ (1) 12 pieces of fruit

____ (2) 50 pieces of fruit

____ (3) 60 pieces of fruit

____ (4) 62 pieces of fruit

____ (5) 102 pieces of fruit

14. Mary and Fred shared a pizza. Mary ate $\frac{1}{3}$ of the pizza and Fred ate $\frac{1}{3}$ of the pizza. How much of the pizza was eaten altogether?

____ (1) $\frac{1}{3}$ of the pizza

____ (2) $\frac{1}{2}$ of the pizza

____ (3) $\frac{2}{3}$ of the pizza

____ (4) $\frac{3}{4}$ of the pizza

____ (5) $1\frac{1}{3}$ of the pizza

15. For lunch, Joe bought a ham and cheese sandwich for $2.65, a carton of milk for $.55, and a package of cookies for $.69. How much did he spend for lunch?

_____ (1) $2.79
_____ (2) $3.20
_____ (3) $3.33
_____ (4) $3.79
_____ (5) $3.89

16. On a coed softball team, 25% of the members are women. What percent of the members are men?

_____ (1) 10%
_____ (2) 20%
_____ (3) 30%
_____ (4) 50%
_____ (5) 75%

17. Gary planted a garden in a plot that measured 50 ft by 25 ft. What is the area of the garden plot?

_____ (1) 75 sq ft
_____ (2) 125 sq ft
_____ (3) 750 sq ft
_____ (4) 1,250 sq ft
_____ (5) 1,250 sq yd

18. Mr. and Mrs. Brown helped their daughter Tisha sell candy bars for her school's marching band. Mrs. Brown sold 15 candy bars at her job, and Mr. Brown sold 23 bars at his job. Tisha sold 9 while going door to door in the neighborhood. How many more candy bars did Mr. and Mrs. Brown sell than their daughter?

_____ (1) 9 bars
_____ (2) 19 bars
_____ (3) 29 bars
_____ (4) 38 bars
_____ (5) 48 bars

19. A cherry pie was divided into 6 equal pieces. How much of the pie was in each serving?

_____ (1) $\frac{1}{8}$ of the pie
_____ (2) $\frac{1}{6}$ of the pie
_____ (3) $\frac{1}{3}$ of the pie
_____ (4) $\frac{1}{4}$ of the pie
_____ (5) $\frac{1}{2}$ of the pie

20. Mrs. Torres owns a fabric shop. She donated $30\frac{1}{3}$ feet of ribbon for the Spring Concert. Each girl in the chorus wore a piece of ribbon $2\frac{1}{3}$ feet long. How many girls were in the chorus?

_____ (1) 13 girls

_____ (2) 14 girls

_____ (3) 15 girls

_____ (4) 17 girls

_____ (5) 18 girls

21. John and Martha Schoel planted a garden with 6 rows of corn. Each row had 24 stalks. How many stalks of corn did they have in all?

_____ (1) 30 stalks

_____ (2) 48 stalks

_____ (3) 124 stalks

_____ (4) 144 stalks

_____ (5) 150 stalks

22. On a recent trip, Henry drove 780 miles in two days. His car averages 25 miles per gallon. He paid $1.19 a gallon for gas. How much did he spend on gasoline for that trip? (Round to the nearest cent.)

_____ (1) $31.20

_____ (2) $37.13

_____ (3) $37.23

_____ (4) $361.28

_____ (5) $371.28

23. For a weekend barbeque, Mr. Warren bought 3 lb of halibut and $6\frac{1}{3}$ lb of salmon steaks to grill outside. If 14 people all ate the same amount of fish, how much did each person eat?

_____ (1) $\frac{1}{2}$ lb

_____ (2) $\frac{2}{3}$ lb

_____ (3) $\frac{5}{6}$ lb

_____ (4) 1 lb

_____ (5) $1\frac{1}{2}$ lb

24. Hal took his 2 children and 2 of their friends out for ice cream. A single-dip cone costs $.65 and a double-dip cone costs $.95. All the children had double-dip cones. How much did Hal spend on the ice cream?

_____ (1) $2.60

_____ (2) $2.90

_____ (3) $3.20

_____ (4) $3.60

_____ (5) $3.80

When you finish the test, compare your answers with those in _Answers and Solutions_ on page 7. Then complete the chart on page 6 by checking the numbers of the problems you got wrong.

SKILL PREVIEW CHART

The chart will show you which math skills you need to pay special attention to. Reread each problem you got wrong. Then look at the appropriate sections of the book for help in figuring out the right answers.

SKILLS	TEST QUESTIONS	STRATEGIES FOR SUCCESS
The test, like this book, focuses on the skills below.	Check (✔) the problems you got wrong.	Preview what you will learn in this book. Learn how to get the right answers.
Addition and Subtraction of Whole Numbers	___ 1 ___ 6 ___ 12 ___ 18	See pages 12–13 STRATEGIES FOR SUCCESS ● Choosing the Operation
Multiplication and Division of Whole Numbers	___ 2 ___ 7 ___ 13 ___ 21	See pages 26–27 STRATEGIES FOR SUCCESS ● Making a Plan
Solving Problems that Involve Fractions	___ 3 ___ 8 ___ 14 ___ 19 ___ 20 ___ 23	See pages 44–45 STRATEGIES FOR SUCCESS ● Solving Problems with a Hidden Step
Solving Problems that Involve Decimals	___ 4 ___ 9 ___ 15 ___ 22 ___ 24	See pages 80–81 STRATEGIES FOR SUCCESS ● Making Problems Easier to Work With
Solving Problems that Involve Percent	___ 5 ___ 10 ___ 16	See pages 98–99 STRATEGIES FOR SUCCESS ● Solving Problems with Several Steps
Solving Problems that Involve Measurement	___ 11 ___ 17	See pages 116–117 STRATEGIES FOR SUCCESS ● Reading, Planning, Solving, and Checking

Answers and Solutions

Page 1

1. (1) 72 miles

```
  4 5 7
− 3 8 5
    7 2
```

2. (2) $150

```
        $6 0 0            $1 5 0
    3 )$1,8 0 0        4 )$6 0 0
        1 8                 4
          0 0               2 0
          0 0               2 0
            0                  0
            0                  0
```

3. (3) 36 ft

$$4\tfrac{1}{2} \times 8 = \frac{9}{2} \times \frac{\overset{4}{8}}{\underset{1}{1}} = 36$$

4. (4) 28.5 hr

```
                 2 8.5
  6.5 0.)1 8 5.2 5.0
         1 3 0 0
           5 5 2 5
           5 2 0 0
             3 2 5 0
             3 2 5 0
```

Page 2

5. (4) $75.84   10% = 0.10

```
  $7 9.5 0        $7 9.5 0
  × 0.1 0        −     7.9 5
  0 0 0 0         $7 1.5 5
  7 9 5 0
  $7.9 5 0 0
```

6% = 0.06

```
  $7 1.5 5              $7 1.5 5
  × 0.0 6            +     4.2 9
  $4.2 9 3 0 → $4.29    $7 5.8 4
```

6. (5) 8 dogs

```
    5
  + 3
    8
```

7. (3) 263 cars

```
           2 6 3
  4 )1,0 5 2
       8
       2 5
       2 4
         1 2
         1 2
```

8. (5) $4\tfrac{11}{24}$ million gallons

$$8\tfrac{5}{8} \qquad\qquad 8\tfrac{15}{24}$$
$$-\,4\tfrac{1}{6} \qquad\qquad -\,4\tfrac{4}{24}$$
$$\overline{} \qquad\qquad \overline{\;\;4\tfrac{11}{24}}$$

9. (4) $7.63

```
  $2 0          $5 0.0 0
    2 0       −   4 2.3 7
  + 1 0          $  7.6 3
  $5 0
```

Page 3

10. (2) $9.00   25% = 0.25

```
  $3 5.9 8
  × 0.2 5
  1 7 9 9 0
  7 1 9 6
  $8.9 9 5 0 → $9.00
```

11. (1) 2 hr 30 min   7:30 a.m. to noon:

```
    12 hr              11 hr 60 min
  −  7 hr 30 min     −  7 hr 30 min
                         4 hr 30 min
```

noon to 6 p.m. is 6 hours

```
    4 hr 30 min        10 hr 30 min
  + 6 hr             −  8 hr
   10 hr 30 min         2 hr 30 min
```

12. (2) 48 gallons

$$\begin{array}{r} 5\,0\,0 \\ -\ 4\,5\,2 \\ \hline 4\,8 \end{array}$$

13. (4) 62 pieces of fruit

$$\begin{array}{r} 5 \\ \times\,2 \\ \hline 1\,0 \end{array} \quad \begin{array}{r} 1\,0 \\ \times\,5 \\ \hline 5\,0 \end{array} \quad \begin{array}{r} 3 \\ \times\,2 \\ \hline 6 \end{array} \quad \begin{array}{r} 6 \\ \times\,2 \\ \hline 1\,2 \end{array} \quad \begin{array}{r} 5\,0 \\ +\,1\,2 \\ \hline 6\,2 \end{array}$$

14. (3) $\frac{2}{3}$ of the pizza

$$\begin{array}{r} \frac{1}{3} \\ +\ \frac{1}{3} \\ \hline \frac{2}{3} \end{array}$$

Page 4

15. (5) $3.89

$$\begin{array}{r} \$2.6\,5 \\ .5\,5 \\ +\ \ .6\,9 \\ \hline \$3.8\,9 \end{array}$$

16. (5) 75%

$$\begin{array}{r} 1\,0\,0\% \\ -\ \ 2\,5\% \\ \hline 7\,5\% \end{array}$$

17. (4) 1,250 sq ft

$$\begin{array}{r} 5\,0 \\ \times\,2\,5 \\ \hline 2\,5\,0 \\ 1\,0\,0 \\ \hline 1{,}2\,5\,0 \end{array}$$

18. (3) 29 bars

$$\begin{array}{r} 1\,5 \\ +\,2\,3 \\ \hline 3\,8 \end{array} \quad \begin{array}{r} 3\,8 \\ -\ \ 9 \\ \hline 2\,9 \end{array}$$

19. (2) $\frac{1}{6}$ of the pie

Page 5

20. (1) 13 girls

$$30\frac{1}{3} \div 2\frac{1}{3} =$$

$$\frac{91}{3} \div \frac{7}{3} =$$

$$\frac{91}{\cancel{3}} \times \frac{\cancel{3}}{7} = \frac{91}{7} = 13$$

21. (4) 144 stalks

$$\begin{array}{r} 2\,4 \\ \times\,6 \\ \hline 1\,4\,4 \end{array}$$

22. (2) $37.13

$$\begin{array}{r} 3\,1.2 \\ 2\,5\,\overline{)\,7\,8\,0.0} \\ 7\,5 \\ \hline 3\,0 \\ 2\,5 \\ \hline 5\,0 \\ 5\,0 \end{array} \quad \begin{array}{r} \$1.1\,9 \\ \times\,3\,1.2 \\ \hline 2\,3\,8 \\ 1\,1\,9 \\ 3\,5\,7 \\ \hline \$3\,7.1\,2\,8 \rightarrow \$37.13 \end{array}$$

23. (2) $\frac{2}{3}$ lb

$$\begin{array}{r} 3 \\ +\,6\frac{1}{3} \\ \hline 9\frac{1}{3} \end{array} \quad \begin{array}{l} 9\frac{1}{3} \div 14 = \\ \frac{28}{3} \div \frac{14}{1} = \\ \frac{\overset{2}{\cancel{28}}}{3} \times \frac{1}{\underset{1}{\cancel{14}}} = \frac{2}{3} \end{array}$$

24. (5) $3.80

$$\begin{array}{r} \$.9\,5 \\ \times\,4 \\ \hline \$3.8\,0 \end{array}$$

WHOLE NUMBERS

ADDITION AND SUBTRACTION

MATH is a language people use around the world. They may call the numbers by different names, but they do the same thing with them that you do. When you figure out how much food you will need for the week, you are doing math. When you see how much your children have grown, you are doing math. Almost every day, you use math in some way.

In this unit, you will be improving your addition and subtraction skills. You will be given hints to help you solve problems that you find in everyday life.

1. ADDITION AND SUBTRACTION

When doing addition and subtraction problems, it is important to line up the numbers correctly.   When the problem is given as

$$\begin{array}{r} 8\ 7 \\ +\ \ \ 2 \\ \hline \end{array}$$

this is easy.   But if the problem is given as "add 23 and 5," you must rewrite it.

"add 23 and 5"   becomes

$$\begin{array}{c|c|c} & 2 & 3 \\ \hline + & 0 & 5 \\ \hline \end{array}$$

Draw vertical lines or place a zero in the problem to keep your columns straight.   When placing zeros to keep columns straight, place them only to the left of the number.

5 equals 05   5 does *not* equal 50

Remember to add the numbers in the right column first.   If the numbers in one column add up to 10 or more, you must *carry*.

$$\begin{array}{r} 3\ 7 \\ 5 \\ +\ 8\ 2 \\ \hline \end{array}$$ 7 + 5 + 2 = 14   Write the 4 and carry the 1.

$$\begin{array}{c|c|c} & 1 & \\ \hline 3 & 7 \\ 0 & 5 \\ + \ 8 & 2 \\ \hline & 4 \\ \end{array}$$

1 + 3 + 0 + 8 = 12   Write the 12.

$$\begin{array}{c|c|c} & 1 & \\ \hline 3 & 7 \\ 0 & 5 \\ +\ 8 & 2 \\ \hline 1 & 2 & 4 \\ \end{array}$$

Practice.   Add   9 + 34 + 65.
Pick the correct form at the right.
Add the numbers from right to left.
Carry when necessary.

$$\begin{array}{r} 9\ 0 \\ 3\ 4 \\ +\ 6\ 5 \\ \hline \end{array} \qquad \begin{array}{r} 0\ 9 \\ 3\ 4 \\ +\ 6\ 5 \\ \hline \end{array}$$

Compare your answer with the one in *Answers and Solutions* on page 21.

Lining the numbers up is just as important in subtraction as it is in addition.   You can place zeros and draw lines if you wish. In subtraction, remember to *borrow* when you need to.

$$
\begin{array}{r} 3\,2 \\ -\,1\,4 \end{array}
$$

You cannot subtract 4 from 2, so borrow.

32 = 30 + 2

Since 30 = 20 + 10, borrow the 10 to go with the 2.

10 + 2 = 12

$$
\begin{array}{r} {\scriptstyle 2\ 12} \\ \cancel{3}\,\cancel{2} \\ -\,1\,4 \\ \hline 8 \end{array}
\qquad
\begin{array}{r} {\scriptstyle 2\ 12} \\ \cancel{3}\,\cancel{2} \\ -\,1\,4 \\ \hline 1\,8 \end{array}
$$

You may need to borrow more than once when there is a zero.

$$
\begin{array}{r} 8\,0\,1 \\ -\,6\,4\,2 \end{array}
\qquad
\begin{array}{r} {\scriptstyle 7\ 10} \\ \cancel{8}\,\cancel{0}\,1 \\ -\,6\,4\,2 \end{array}
\qquad
\begin{array}{r} {\scriptstyle\ \ \ 9} \\ {\scriptstyle 7\ 10\ 11} \\ \cancel{8}\,\cancel{0}\,\cancel{1} \\ -\,6\,4\,2 \\ \hline 9 \end{array}
\qquad
\begin{array}{r} {\scriptstyle\ \ \ 9} \\ {\scriptstyle 7\ 10\ 11} \\ \cancel{8}\,\cancel{0}\,\cancel{1} \\ -\,6\,4\,2 \\ \hline 5\,9 \end{array}
\qquad
\begin{array}{r} {\scriptstyle\ \ \ 9} \\ {\scriptstyle 7\ 10\ 11} \\ \cancel{8}\,\cancel{0}\,\cancel{1} \\ -\,6\,4\,2 \\ \hline 1\,5\,9 \end{array}
$$

Practice.   Add or subtract.   Then compare your answers with those in *Answers and Solutions* on page 21.

1.
$$
\begin{array}{r} 5\,4 \\ +\,2\,9 \end{array}
$$

2. 7 + 33

3.
$$
\begin{array}{r} 5\,4 \\ -\,2\,9 \end{array}
$$

4.
$$
\begin{array}{r} 3\,9 \\ -\,1\,2 \end{array}
$$

5.
$$
\begin{array}{r} 2\,3\,8 \\ -\ \ 6\,1 \end{array}
$$

6.
$$
\begin{array}{r} 7\,5 \\ -\,2\,3 \end{array}
$$

7.
$$
\begin{array}{r} 7\,0\,6 \\ +\,4\,2\,5 \end{array}
$$

8. 126 + 5 + 28

9.
$$
\begin{array}{r} 4\,0 \\ -\,2\,1 \end{array}
$$

10. 306 − 49

11.
$$
\begin{array}{r} 5\,0\,8 \\ -\ \ 5\,2 \end{array}
$$

12.
$$
\begin{array}{r} 6\,5\,7 \\ 5 \\ +\ \ 9\,4 \end{array}
$$

STRATEGIES FOR SUCCESS

CHOOSING THE OPERATION

Certain words act as a kind of signal. They tell you what operation to use to solve the problem.

STRATEGY: **Look for key words.**

Look for the words that tell you to add or to subtract.

Example 1: What are the key words in this problem?

Rita had $15 and Maria had $17.

How much did they have altogether?

Think about the meaning of the words. *Altogether* tells you to put the two amounts together, in other words to add. Other key words that tell you to add are *plus, sum, in all,* and *total.*

$$\begin{array}{r} \$\,1\,5 \\ +\quad 1\,7 \\ \hline \$\,3\,2 \end{array}$$

Example 2: What are the key words in this problem?

Cora has 8 bus tokens. Roger has 5 tokens. How many more tokens does Cora have than Roger?

The words *more...than* ask you to
compare the numbers 8 and 5. One
number is larger than the other, so you
subtract to find out how much larger.
Other words that tell you to subtract are
minus, difference, less, and *fewer.*

$$
\begin{array}{r}
8 \\
-\ 5 \\
\hline
3
\end{array}
$$

Solve these problems: Use the strategy on page 12.

1. Smith, Hayes, and Eaton ran for mayor. 251 people
   voted for Smith, 732 people voted for Hayes, and 49
   people voted for Eaton. Find the total number of
   people who voted in the election.

- What is the key word? _____
- What is the operation? _____
- What is the answer? _____

2. Alicia Curtis wants to buy a late-model used car for
   $4,500. She can get $1,100 trade-in for her present
   car. How much more will the car cost than what
   she can get for the trade-in?

- What are the key words? _____
- What is the operation? _____
- What is the answer? _____

Check your answers. Read the problems again. Ask
yourself if the answers make sense. Make sure that you
answered the questions.

Compare your answers with those in *Answers and Solutions* on page 21.

Self-Test

Solve these problems. Put an X next to the correct answer. Then compare your answers with those in *Answers and Solutions* on page 21.

Addition word problems.

1. On Monday, Sue mailed 51 letters. On Tuesday, she mailed 76 letters. How many did she mail in all?

    _____ (1) 51 letters

    _____ (2) 70 letters

    _____ (3) 76 letters

    _____ (4) 100 letters

    _____ (5) 127 letters

2. Mrs. Navarro counted the crates on three loading docks. There were 21 crates on the first dock. The next dock had 19 crates, and the last dock had 20 crates. How many crates did she count in all?

    _____ (1) 19 crates

    _____ (2) 21 crates

    _____ (3) 50 crates

    _____ (4) 60 crates

    _____ (5) 70 crates

3. During one week, an automobile company produced 4,807 passenger cars, 6,952 trucks, and 840 vans. How many vehicles did the company produce that week?

    _____ (1) 3,967 vehicles

    _____ (2) 7,439 vehicles

    _____ (3) 12,599 vehicles

    _____ (4) 12,662 vehicles

    _____ (5) 20,159 vehicles

Subtraction word problems.

4. Oliver ran 17 miles in a marathon. Emily dropped out at 12 miles. How many more miles did Oliver run than Emily?

    _____ (1) 3 miles

    _____ (2) 5 miles

    _____ (3) 7 miles

    _____ (4) 12 miles

    _____ (5) 17 miles

5. Ms. Howard's electric bill showed that her family used 6,072 kilowatt hours of electricity in January. In February, they used 4,036 kilowatt hours. How many more kilowatt hours did they use in January than in February?

    _____ (1) 236 kilowatt hours

    _____ (2) 1,108 kilowatt hours

    _____ (3) 1,036 kilowatt hours

    _____ (4) 2,036 kilowatt hours

    _____ (5) 10,108 kilowatt hours

Decide whether to add or subtract.

6. Mr. Bell bought two loads of coal. One load weighed 6,000 pounds. The other weighed 3,000 pounds. How many pounds did he buy altogether?

_____ (1) 900 pounds

_____ (2) 3,000 pounds

_____ (3) 9,000 pounds

_____ (4) 10,000 pounds

_____ (5) 11,000 pounds

7. The new Jackson Theater seats 400 people. The old theater seated only 250. How many more people can the new theater hold?

_____ (1) 150 people

_____ (2) 200 people

_____ (3) 450 people

_____ (4) 600 people

_____ (5) 650 people

8. A clothing manufacturer made 35,000 shirts during the year. He sold a total of 26,500 shirts. How many shirts were not sold?

_____ (1) 6,500 shirts

_____ (2) 7,000 shirts

_____ (3) 7,500 shirts

_____ (4) 8,500 shirts

_____ (5) 51,500 shirts

9. Sid Brown delivers packages in two cities. On one day, he drove 364 miles. On the next day, he drove 250 miles. What was the total number of miles he drove?

_____ (1) 114 miles

_____ (2) 124 miles

_____ (3) 514 miles

_____ (4) 614 miles

_____ (5) 724 miles

10. One week Helen's Country Store sold 160 jars of strawberry jam and 205 jars of blueberry jam. How many more jars of blueberry jam were sold than strawberry jam?

_____ (1) 35 jars

_____ (2) 45 jars

_____ (3) 145 jars

_____ (4) 265 jars

_____ (5) 365 jars

2. TWO-STEP PROBLEMS

Many problems cannot be solved by adding or subtracting just once. You have to add or subtract a second time.

Example:

Sam bought a roll for 37¢ and a pint of milk for 50¢. He gave the cashier 90¢. How much change did he receive?

You can probably solve this problem without any trouble. And the same steps that you use here can be used to solve more complicated problems.

The problem asks how much change he received. You are looking for the balance or what is left over. This means subtraction. It is also true that two things were bought and put together. This means addition. How do you know when to add and when to subtract?

The problem says that Sam bought two things and that he gave the cashier 90¢. Picture the situation and think about what happens in it. First the cashier at the store would *add* the prices of the items Sam bought.

Step 1. addition

$$
\begin{array}{r}
3\,7\ ¢ \quad \text{roll} \\
+\ 5\,0\ ¢ \quad \text{milk} \\
\hline
8\,7\ ¢ \quad \text{total cost of purchases}
\end{array}
$$

Then the cashier would make change. She would *subtract* the total cost of the purchases from the money Sam gave her.

Step 2. subtraction

$$
\begin{array}{r}
9\,0\ ¢ \quad \text{money given to cashier} \\
-\ 8\,7\ ¢ \quad \text{total cost of purchases} \\
\hline
3\ ¢ \quad \text{change}
\end{array}
$$

There are sometimes different ways to do the same problem.

Another way to solve the problem on page 16 is to use subtraction twice.

Step 1.   9 0 ¢   *Step 2.*   5 3 ¢

            − 3 7 ¢   − 5 0 ¢

             5 3 ¢   3 ¢

In some problems, the units of measure are different. Step 1 will be to change them to the same kind of units. Before doing addition or subtraction, the units of measure must be the same.

Example:

Christine was making a new shirt for her daughter. She had one yard of cloth. She used two feet of the cloth. How much did she have left?

Step 1. 1 yard = 3 feet   *Step 2.*   3 ft

                                            − 2 ft

                                            1 ft

Christine started with one *yard* of cloth and ended up with one *foot* of cloth.

*F*OR YOUR INFORMATION

Units of measure are used with numbers to tell how something is measured. Here are some equivalent units of measure and their abbreviations.

1 yard = 3 feet   or 1 yd = 3 ft (3′)

1 foot = 12 inches or 1 ft = 12 in. or 1′ = 12″

1 pound = 16 ounces or 1 lb = 16 oz

Self-Test

Solve these problems.   Pux an X next to the correct answer.   Then compare your answers with those in *Answers and Solutions* on page 21.

Solve these two-step problems.

1. Thomas Rivera had 32 bins of packages to sort.   He sorted 10 bins the first hour and 5 the next.   How many bins did he still have left to sort?

   _____ (1) 5 bins

   _____ (2) 15 bins

   _____ (3) 17 bins

   _____ (4) 42 bins

   _____ (5) 47 bins

2. Mrs. Bessy needs 4 oz of cream cheese for a dip.   She has 1 lb of cream cheese in her refrigerator.   How many ounces will she have left after she makes the dip?

   _____ (1) 1 oz

   _____ (2) 2 oz

   _____ (3) 8 oz

   _____ (4) 12 oz

   _____ (5) 16 oz

3. Last year, Ben Roberts used a total of 950 gallons of oil in January and February.   This year, he used 350 gallons in January and 275 gallons in February.   How many fewer gallons did he use this year?

   _____ (1) 275 gallons

   _____ (2) 325 gallons

   _____ (3) 625 gallons

   _____ (4) 1,025 gallons

   _____ (5) 1,575 gallons

4. Paul wants to bake a batch of cookies for his softball party.   The recipe calls for 1 lb of butter.   Paul has only 12 oz on hand.   How many more ounces does he need?

   _____ (1) 4 oz

   _____ (2) 8 oz

   _____ (3) 12 oz

   _____ (4) 16 oz

   _____ (5) 28 oz

5. Al Wong had a yard sale for 2 weekends.   The first Saturday he made $35.   The second weekend he made $101.   Altogether he made $179.   How much did he make on the first Sunday?

   _____ (1) $24

   _____ (2) $43

   _____ (3) $78

   _____ (4) $137

   _____ (5) $143

6. Marta was making clothes for her daughter's doll. She found a piece of ribbon that was 1 foot long. She used 7 inches of ribbon for the doll's dress. How much ribbon did she have left?

_____ (1) 4″
_____ (2) 5″
_____ (3) 7″
_____ (4) 12″
_____ (5) 19″

7. Bill Schneider checked his grain barrel and found he had only 14 pounds left. That night, he fed 9 pounds to his chickens. The next day, he bought 100 pounds of grain and added it to the barrel. How much grain was then in the barrel?

_____ (1) 25 lb
_____ (2) 77 lb
_____ (3) 105 lb
_____ (4) 109 lb
_____ (5) 123 lb

8. In their spare time, Cleon and his brother work on cars. Last week Cleon had 9 spark plugs on hand and he bought 12 more. He sold 8 spark plugs to his brother. How many spark plugs did Cleon have then?

_____ (1) 11 spark plugs
_____ (2) 13 spark plugs
_____ (3) 20 spark plugs
_____ (4) 21 spark plugs
_____ (5) 29 spark plugs

9. Mrs. Russo went to the shoe repair shop and paid $23 to have her shoes resoled. Then she went next door and bought a bag of potatoes for $4. Before her purchases, she had $45. How much did Mrs. Russo have after her purchases?

_____ (1) $18
_____ (2) $26
_____ (3) $27
_____ (4) $28
_____ (5) $72

10. Laurence King drives a truck. He is paid overtime for every hour over 40 hours that he works in one week. He worked 9 hours on Monday, 10 hours on Tuesday, and 29 hours the rest of the week. How many hours of overtime did he work?

_____ (1) 8 hours
_____ (2) 12 hours
_____ (3) 19 hours
_____ (4) 40 hours
_____ (5) 48 hours

11. At a local firehouse one year, calls were answered on 317 days. On how many days were calls not received? (1 year = 365 days)

_____ (1) 32 days

_____ (2) 38 days

_____ (3) 48 days

_____ (4) 52 days

_____ (5) 58 days

12. Tara Jackson writes parking tickets. By Wednesday of last week, she had already written 192 tickets. On Thursday, she wrote 67 tickets and on Friday, 59 tickets. What was her weekly total?

_____ (1) 66 tickets

_____ (2) 126 tickets

_____ (3) 192 tickets

_____ (4) 308 tickets

_____ (5) 318 tickets

13. The Uptown Theater has two shows a night. 134 people saw the first show. 153 people entered the theater for the second show. If 167 people left at the end of the second show, how many left after the first show?

_____ (1) 14 people

_____ (2) 19 people

_____ (3) 120 people

_____ (4) 130 people

_____ (5) 134 people

14. Lillian Turner takes home $162 a week from her job. She pays $48 a week for day-care for her son. She also spends $9 a week on transportation. How much does she have left?

_____ (1) $57

_____ (2) $95

_____ (3) $105

_____ (4) $162

_____ (5) $219

15. A restaurant ordered 53 pounds of tomatoes and 27 pounds of cucumbers. They also ordered lemons. Their total order weighed 105 pounds. How much did the lemons weigh?

_____ (1) 15 lb

_____ (2) 25 lb

_____ (3) 26 lb

_____ (4) 125 lb

_____ (5) 185 lb

Answers and Solutions

Page 10   Practice

```
    0 9
    3 4
  + 6 5
  1 0 8
```

Page 11   Practice

1. 83	**2.** 40	**3.** 25
4. 27	**5.** 177	**6.** 52
7. 1,131	**8.** 159	**9.** 19
10. 257	**11.** 456	**12.** 756

Page 13   Strategies For Success

1.
- total
- addition
- 1,032 people

```
    2 5 1
    7 3 2
  +   4 9
  1,0 3 2
```

2.
- how much more
- subtraction
- $3,400

```
  $ 4,5 0 0
  −   1,1 0 0
  $ 3,4 0 0
```

Page 14   Self-Test

1. (5) 127 letters

```
    5 1
  + 7 6
  1 2 7
```

2. (4) 60 crates

```
    2 1
    1 9
  + 2 0
    6 0
```

3. (3) 12,599 vehicles

```
    4,8 0 7
    6,9 5 2
  +   8 4 0
  1 2,5 9 9
```

4. (2) 5 miles

```
    1 7
  − 1 2
      5
```

5. (4) 2,036 kwh

```
    6,0 7 2
  − 4,0 3 6
    2,0 3 6
```

Page 15   Self-Test

6. (3) 9,000 pounds

```
    6,0 0 0
  + 3,0 0 0
    9,0 0 0
```

7. (1) 150 people

```
    4 0 0
  − 2 5 0
    1 5 0
```

8. (4) 8,500 shirts

```
    3 5,0 0 0
  − 2 6,5 0 0
      8,5 0 0
```

9. (4) 614 miles

```
    3 6 4
  + 2 5 0
    6 1 4
```

10. (2) 45 jars

```
    2 0 5
  − 1 6 0
      4 5
```

Page 18   Self-Test

1. (3) 17 bins

```
    1 0        3 2
  +   5      − 1 5
    1 5        1 7
```

2. (4) 12 oz   1 lb = 16 oz

```
    1 6
  −   4
    1 2
```

3. (2) 325 gallons

$$
\begin{array}{r}
3\ 5\ 0 \\
+\ 2\ 7\ 5 \\
\hline
6\ 2\ 5
\end{array}
\qquad
\begin{array}{r}
9\ 5\ 0 \\
-\ 6\ 2\ 5 \\
\hline
3\ 2\ 5
\end{array}
$$

4. (1) 4 oz   1 lb = 16 oz

$$
\begin{array}{r}
1\ 6 \\
-\ 1\ 2 \\
\hline
4
\end{array}
$$

5. (2) $43

$$
\begin{array}{r}
\$\ \ \ 3\ 5 \\
+\ 1\ 0\ 1 \\
\hline
\$\ 1\ 3\ 6
\end{array}
\qquad
\begin{array}{r}
\$\ 1\ 7\ 9 \\
-\ 1\ 3\ 6 \\
\hline
\$\ \ \ 4\ 3
\end{array}
$$

Page 19   Self-Test

6. (2) 5″   1 ft = 12 in.

$$
\begin{array}{r}
1\ 2 \\
-\ \ \ 7 \\
\hline
5
\end{array}
$$

7. (3) 105 lb

$$
\begin{array}{r}
1\ 4 \\
-\ \ \ 9 \\
\hline
5
\end{array}
\qquad
\begin{array}{r}
1\ 0\ 0 \\
+\ \ \ \ 5 \\
\hline
1\ 0\ 5
\end{array}
$$

8. (2) 13 spark plugs

$$
\begin{array}{r}
1\ 2 \\
+\ \ \ 9 \\
\hline
2\ 1
\end{array}
\qquad
\begin{array}{r}
2\ 1 \\
+\ \ \ 8 \\
\hline
1\ 3
\end{array}
$$

9. (1) $18

$$
\begin{array}{r}
\$\ 2\ 3 \\
+\ \ \ 4 \\
\hline
2\ 7
\end{array}
\qquad
\begin{array}{r}
\$\ 4\ 5 \\
-\ 2\ 7 \\
\hline
1\ 8
\end{array}
$$

10. (1) 8 hours

$$
\begin{array}{r}
9 \\
1\ 0 \\
+\ 2\ 9 \\
\hline
4\ 8
\end{array}
\qquad
\begin{array}{r}
4\ 8 \\
-\ 4\ 0 \\
\hline
8
\end{array}
$$

Page 20   Self-Test

11. (3) 48 days
1 year = 365 days

$$
\begin{array}{r}
3\ 6\ 5 \\
-\ 3\ 1\ 7 \\
\hline
4\ 8
\end{array}
$$

12. (5) 318 tickets

$$
\begin{array}{r}
1\ 9\ 2 \\
+\ \ 6\ 7 \\
\hline
2\ 5\ 9
\end{array}
\qquad
\begin{array}{r}
2\ 5\ 9 \\
+\ \ 5\ 9 \\
\hline
3\ 1\ 8
\end{array}
$$

13. (3) 120 people

$$
\begin{array}{r}
1\ 6\ 7 \\
-\ 1\ 5\ 3 \\
\hline
1\ 4
\end{array}
\qquad
\begin{array}{r}
1\ 3\ 4 \\
+\ \ 1\ 4 \\
\hline
1\ 2\ 0
\end{array}
$$

14. (3) $105

$$
\begin{array}{r}
\$\ 1\ 6\ 2 \\
-\ \ \ 4\ 8 \\
\hline
\$\ 1\ 1\ 4
\end{array}
\qquad
\begin{array}{r}
\$\ 1\ 1\ 4 \\
-\ \ \ \ 9 \\
\hline
\$\ 1\ 0\ 5
\end{array}
$$

15. (2) 25 lb

$$
\begin{array}{r}
2\ 7 \\
+\ 5\ 3 \\
\hline
8\ 0
\end{array}
\qquad
\begin{array}{r}
1\ 0\ 5 \\
-\ \ 8\ 0 \\
\hline
2\ 5
\end{array}
$$

WHOLE NUMBERS

MULTIPLICATION AND DIVISION

IN the last unit, you worked with problems that required addition and subtraction. But for many situations in your life you will need to use multiplication and division. In this unit, you will practice these skills.

You will also solve problems that take several steps to solve, and that ask you to decide whether to use addition, subtraction, multiplication, or division.

1. MULTIPLICATION AND DIVISION

To multiply large numbers, you use multiplication and addition. Begin multiplying from the right. As in addition, you carry. Drawing vertical lines will help keep columns straight for addition.

3 2	Multiply by	3 2	Now multiply by	3 2	Then	3 2	
× 2 8	the first digit	× 2 8	the next digit	× 2 8	add.	× 2 8	
	to the right, 8.	2 5 6	to the left, 2.	2 5 6		2 5 6	
			Put the result	6 4		+ 6 4	
			one place to			8 9 6	
			the left.				

Practice. Multiply. Then compare your answers with those in *Answers and Solutions* on page 35.

1. 5 8	2. 4 6	3. 3 8	4. 9 6	5. 5 3 5	6. 8 2 2
× 9	× 1 9	× 2 9	× 5 1	× 1 8 9	× 4 0 6

There are four steps in division. They are repeated as often as necessary.

Example:

Divide.	Multiply.	Subtract.	Bring down.

```
        5           ×   5            5              5
    3)1 6 2      3)1 6 2         3)1 6 2        3)1 6 2
                   1 5            - 1 5            1 5
                                     1             1 2
```

Repeat.

```
        5 4           5 4            5 4         There is
    3)1 6 2       3)1 6 2        3)1 6 2         nothing to
      1 5           1 5            1 5           bring down,
        1 2           1 2            1 2         so you
                      1 2            1 2         are done.
                                      0
```

When dividing by a 2-digit number, it is useful to round both numbers.   This will help tell you where to put the first digit in the answer. It will also give you an estimate you can compare with your answer.

28)1456

28 is almost 30.
1456 is almost 1500.
Think of 30
into 1500.

```
      5 2
28)1 4 5 6
   1 4 0
     5 6
     5 6
        0
```

```
      5 0
30)1 5 0 0
   1 5 0
     0 0
     0 0
        0
```

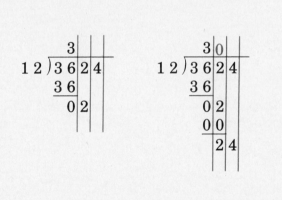

In some division problems, zero will appear as part of the answer.   Be sure to include it.   For longer problems, it may be helpful to draw vertical lines.

12)3 6 2 4

```
        3|
12)3 6|2|4
   3 6|
   0 2|
```

```
        3|0
12)3 6|2|4
   3 6|
   0 2|
   0 0|
     2 4
```

```
        3|0|2
12)3 6|2|4
   3 6|
   0 2|
   0 0|
     2 4
     2 4
        0
```

Practice. Divide.   Then compare your answers with those in *Answers and Solutions* on page 35.

1. 8)1 9 2   **2.** 7)3 6 4   **3.** 2 3)8 2 8

4. 1 8)6 3 0   **5.** 9 1)2 9 1 2   **6.** 4 1)8 5 6 9

STRATEGIES FOR SUCCESS

MAKING A PLAN

Sometimes the key words in a problem aren't obvious.   Then it helps to draw a simple picture of the problem.   A picture can help you plan how to solve the problem.

STRATEGY: Picture the situation.

For simple problems, you can picture the situation in your head.   It's a good idea to put a sketch on paper for more complicated problems.

Example 1:   Draw a picture to illustrate this problem.

One book costs $8.   How much would 6 books cost?

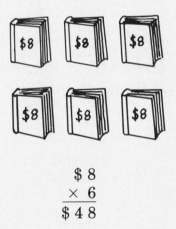

From the picture, you can see that you have the same thing repeated several times.   Adding the same thing over and over is the idea behind multiplication.

$$\begin{array}{r} \$\,8 \\ \times\ 6 \\ \hline \$\,4\,8 \end{array}$$

Example 2:   Draw a picture to illustrate this problem.

Five boxes of paper weigh 15 pounds.   How much does one box of paper weigh?

From the picture, you can see that the 15 pounds must be divided up between the 5 boxes. Each box will weigh the same. So you divide 15 by 5.

$$5\overline{)15}$$
$$\underline{15}$$

with quotient 3.

Solve these problems: Use the strategy above.

1. If one can of paint weighs 7 pounds, how much do 8 cans of the same paint weigh?

- Draw a picture.
- What is the operation? _____
- What is the answer? _____

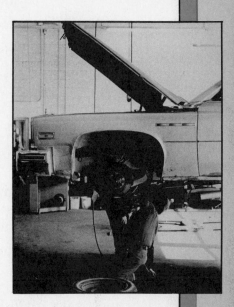

2. Hester, Sue, and Tanya went to the movies. Tanya paid for all three tickets. She paid $15. How much did each ticket cost?

- Draw a picture.
- What is the operation? _____
- What is the answer? _____

3. Phil bought a headlight and a tire for his car. The headlight cost $5 and the tire cost $33. He paid the mechanic $5 for labor. How much money did Phil spend?

- Draw a picture.
- What is the operation? _____
- What is the answer? _____

Check your answers. Read the problems again. Ask yourself if the answers make sense. Make sure that you answered the questions.

Compare your answers with those in *Answers and Solutions* on page 35.

$\mathcal{S}$elf-Test

Multiplication word problems.

1. Louise types 71 words per minute. How many words can she type in 15 minutes?

    _____ (1) 355 words

    _____ (2) 1,065 words

    _____ (3) 1,071 words

    _____ (4) 2,065 words

    _____ (5) 3,000 words

2. There are 3 feet in 1 yard.   How many feet are there in 35 yards?

    _____ (1) 4 ft

    _____ (2) 36 ft

    _____ (3) 38 ft

    _____ (4) 98 ft

    _____ (5) 105 ft

3. During a sale, a store sold 125 clock radios for $19 apiece.   How much money did the store receive for the clock radios?

    _____ (1) $1,050

    _____ (2) $1,125

    _____ (3) $1,250

    _____ (4) $2,375

    _____ (5) $3,375

Division word problems.

4. An eight-pound block of cheese costs $16.   How much is the cheese per pound?

    _____ (1) $2

    _____ (2) $3

    _____ (3) $8

    _____ (4) $24

    _____ (5) $128

5. Bill Carlson has bought a car.   The total price, including interest, is $5,616.   If he makes 36 payments to pay off the loan, what must he pay each month?

    _____ (1) $106

    _____ (2) $140

    _____ (3) $156

    _____ (4) $165

    _____ (5) $172

Decide whether to multiply or divide.

6. Roberta earns $263 a week.   How much will she earn altogether in 16 weeks?
   ____ (1) $263
   ____ (2) $279
   ____ (3) $2,308
   ____ (4) $4,208
   ____ (5) $4,408

7. Mrs. Salazar wants to save $1,000 to buy a canoe.   She plans to save $25 a week.   How many weeks will it take her to save the money to buy the canoe?
   ____ (1) 10 weeks
   ____ (2) 20 weeks
   ____ (3) 25 weeks
   ____ (4) 40 weeks
   ____ (5) 100 weeks

8. If a box holds 50 envelopes, how many envelopes will there be in 28 boxes?
   ____ (1) 22 envelopes
   ____ (2) 78 envelopes
   ____ (3) 140 envelopes
   ____ (4) 1,000 envelopes
   ____ (5) 1,400 envelopes

9. A case holds 24 bottles of soda.   How many cases will 216 bottles fill?
   ____ (1) 5 cases
   ____ (2) 9 cases
   ____ (3) 24 cases
   ____ (4) 216 cases
   ____ (5) 5,184 cases

10. Lala Pelkey is a salesperson.   She drove 240 miles last week.   At 16 miles per gallon, how many gallons of gasoline did she use?
    ____ (1) 11 gallons
    ____ (2) 12 gallons
    ____ (3) 15 gallons
    ____ (4) 17 gallons
    ____ (5) 25 gallons

2. SOLVING PROBLEMS WITH MANY STEPS

Some problems require many steps to solve. You might have to add and subtract; or add and multiply; or add, then divide, and then subtract. Each step is usually easy. But deciding what to do can be difficult. It is important to read the whole problem first. Get a picture of what is happening. If possible, imagine yourself in the situation. Also, ask yourself how large an answer would make sense. Look at this problem.

Example:

Julio sold an average of 6 television sets a day for Monday through Friday. The same week, Norman sold 27 sets. Who sold more sets?

The problem asks you to compare Julio's sales with Norman's sales. To do so, you will subtract. But that will be the *last* step. First, find out how many sets Julio sold.

Step 1. Julio sold an average of 6 sets a day for 5 days. Find the total number of sets he sold. Multiply.

$$\begin{array}{r} 6 \\ \times\ 5 \\ \hline 3\,0 \end{array}$$

Step 2. Compare the number of sets sold by Julio with the number of sets sold by Norman. Subtract.

$$\begin{array}{r} 3\,0 \\ -\ 2\,7 \\ \hline 3 \end{array}$$

Julio sold 3 more television sets than Norman did.

FOR YOUR INFORMATION

When the problem says "an *average* of 6 television sets a day for Monday through Friday," you know that the total number of TVs sold is the same as if 6 sets were sold each day. So to find the total you can multiply 5 times 6.

Suppose a salesperson sold 1 TV on Monday, 4 TVs on Tuesday, 6 TVs on Wednesday, 3 TVs on Thursday, and 6 TVs on Friday. To find the average, add up the total number of TVs sold.

$$1 + 4 + 6 + 3 + 6 = 20$$

Then divide the total number (20) by the number of days.

$$20 \div 5 = 4$$

The *average* number of television sets sold each day is 4.

Practice. Solve the problem. Then compare your answers with those in *Answers and Solutions* on page 36.

In 4 basketball games, Henry averaged 12 points a game. In those same 4 games, Clyde scored 15 points, 10 points, 5 points and 14 points. Who scored more points?

To find out how many points Henry scored in the 4 games, would you add, subtract, multiply, or divide? _____

To find out how many points Clyde scored in the 4 games, would you add, subtract, multiply, or divide? _____

To compare how many points the two men scored, would you add, subtract, multiply, or divide? _____

Self-Test

Problems with many steps.

1. Ron worked for 6 hours on Monday, 4 hours on Tuesday, and 3 hours on Wednesday. Nara worked for 5 hours on Thursday and 3 on Friday. How many hours less did Nara work than Ron?

_____ (1) 3 hr

_____ (2) 5 hr

_____ (3) 8 hr

_____ (4) 13 hr

_____ (5) 21 hr

2. Flora took a series of aptitude tests. Her scores on five tests were 42, 48, 46, 50, and 54. What was her average score?

_____ (1) 38

_____ (2) 48

_____ (3) 190

_____ (4) 210

_____ (5) 250

3. At the shoe factory, Vito is paid $3 for every case of shoes he stitches. This week he stitched 20 cases on Monday, 22 on Tuesday, 18 on Wednesday, 23 on Thursday, and 21 on Friday. How much was he paid altogether for his week's work?

_____ (1) $3

_____ (2) $20

_____ (3) $104

_____ (4) $312

_____ (5) $412

4. Millie Cruz earns $402 a week. She has the following amounts taken out of her paycheck: $60 for federal tax; $12 for state tax; and $26 for social security. What is her take-home pay?

_____ (1) $98

_____ (2) $304

_____ (3) $306

_____ (4) $398

_____ (5) $402

5. Ali has a piece of lumber 102 inches long. He needs 10 pieces of lumber 17 inches long. How much more lumber does he need?

_____ (1) 68 in.

_____ (2) 72 in.

_____ (3) 102 in.

_____ (4) 122 in.

_____ (5) 170 in.

6. Skip and Bob will need 6,000 nails to finish the house they are building. They have 20 pounds of nails on hand. If there are 30 nails to a pound, how many more pounds of nails will they have to buy?

_____ (1) 50 lb

_____ (2) 60 lb

_____ (3) 180 lb

_____ (4) 200 lb

_____ (5) 280 lb

7. Helen had a new carburetor put in her car. It took the mechanic 4 hours to put in the new part. Labor costs $20 per hour. The new part cost $135, and the tax was $11. What was the total bill for the new carburetor?

_____ (1) $80

_____ (2) $146

_____ (3) $166

_____ (4) $215

_____ (5) $226

8. On a three-day trip, Vernon drove 150 miles on each of the first two days and 300 miles on the third day. What was the average distance that he drove each day?

_____ (1) 100 miles

_____ (2) 200 miles

_____ (3) 300 miles

_____ (4) 450 miles

_____ (5) 600 miles

9. Tamara needed a piece of wood 36 inches long. She had a board that was 5 feet long. After she cut off what she needed, how many feet were left?

_____ (1) 2 ft

_____ (2) 3 ft

_____ (3) 8 ft

_____ (4) 24 ft

_____ (5) 60 ft

10. Albert makes lamps and sells them for $25 each. Each lamp needs 6 feet of electric wire. Last month he used 18 yards of electric wire to make lamps. How much money did he get for the lamps?

_____ (1) $54

_____ (2) $75

_____ (3) $154

_____ (4) $185

_____ (5) $225

11. A freight car holds 260 cases. Each case weighs 105 pounds. What is the total weight of the cases in the freight car?

_____ (1) 365 lb

_____ (2) 2,730 lb

_____ (3) 3,900 lb

_____ (4) 17,300 lb

_____ (5) 27,300 lb

12. Dean bought a television set that cost $145. He made a down payment of $45 and paid the rest in weekly payments of $20. How many weeks did he make the payments?

_____ (1) 2 weeks

_____ (2) 3 weeks

_____ (3) 5 weeks

_____ (4) 6 weeks

_____ (5) 7 weeks

13. Ms. Perkins has a shop that sells accessories. She sells scarves for $3, $5, and $7. During one week she sold 5 of the $3 scarves and 7 of the $7 scarves. Altogether she sold $94 worth of scarves that week. How many of the $5 scarves did she sell?

_____ (1) 3 scarves

_____ (2) 4 scarves

_____ (3) 5 scarves

_____ (4) 6 scarves

_____ (5) 7 scarves

14. In a community, an average of 7,500 quarts of milk are consumed each day. Find the number of quarts consumed during a month that has 31 days.

_____ (1) 7,531 qt

_____ (2) 30,000 qt

_____ (3) 212,500 qt

_____ (4) 232,500 qt

_____ (5) 242,500 qt

15. An auto parts store bought 5,000 quarts of oil. Five quarts of oil and an oil filter were sold together as an "oil change kit" during a sale. 872 "oil change kits" were sold. How many quarts of oil were left over?

_____ (1) 640 qt

_____ (2) 1,640 qt

_____ (3) 4,061 qt

_____ (4) 4,128 qt

_____ (5) 740 qt

Answers and Solutions

Page 24   Practice

1.
$$\begin{array}{r} 58 \\ \times\ \ 9 \\ \hline 522 \end{array}$$

2.
$$\begin{array}{r} 46 \\ \times\ 19 \\ \hline 414 \\ 46\ \ \\ \hline 874 \end{array}$$

3.
$$\begin{array}{r} 38 \\ \times\ 29 \\ \hline 342 \\ 76\ \ \\ \hline 1,102 \end{array}$$

4.
$$\begin{array}{r} 96 \\ \times\ 51 \\ \hline 96 \\ 480\ \ \\ \hline 4,896 \end{array}$$

5.
$$\begin{array}{r} 535 \\ \times\ 189 \\ \hline 4815 \\ 4280\ \ \\ 535\ \ \ \\ \hline 101,115 \end{array}$$

6.
$$\begin{array}{r} 822 \\ \times\ 406 \\ \hline 4932 \\ 000\ \ \\ 3288\ \ \ \\ \hline 333,732 \end{array}$$

Page 25   Practice

1.
$$\begin{array}{r} 24 \\ 8\overline{)192} \\ \underline{16}\ \ \\ 32 \\ \underline{32} \end{array}$$

2.
$$\begin{array}{r} 52 \\ 7\overline{)364} \\ \underline{35}\ \ \\ 14 \\ \underline{14} \end{array}$$

3.
$$\begin{array}{r} 36 \\ 23\overline{)828} \\ \underline{69}\ \ \\ 138 \\ \underline{138} \end{array}$$

4.
$$\begin{array}{r} 35 \\ 18\overline{)630} \\ \underline{54}\ \ \\ 90 \\ \underline{90} \end{array}$$

5.
$$\begin{array}{r} 32 \\ 91\overline{)2912} \\ \underline{273}\ \ \\ 182 \\ \underline{182} \end{array}$$

6.
$$\begin{array}{r} 209 \\ 41\overline{)8569} \\ \underline{82}\ \ \ \\ 36 \\ 00 \\ 369 \\ \underline{369} \end{array}$$

Page 27   Strategies For Success

1.

- multiplication
- 56 pounds

$$\begin{array}{r} 7 \\ \times\ 8 \\ \hline 56 \end{array}$$

2.

ADMIT ONE
ADMIT ONE
ADMIT ONE
} $15

- division
- $5

$$\begin{array}{r} 5 \\ 3\overline{)15} \end{array}$$

3.

$5
$5
$33
} $43

- addition
- $43

$$\begin{array}{r} 5 \\ 5 \\ +\ 33 \\ \hline 43 \end{array}$$

Page 28   Self-Test

1. (2) 1,065 words
$$\begin{array}{r} 71 \\ \times\ 15 \\ \hline 355 \\ 71\ \ \\ \hline 1,065 \end{array}$$

2. (5) 105 ft
$$\begin{array}{r} 35 \\ \times\ 3 \\ \hline 105 \end{array}$$

3. (4) $2,375
$$\begin{array}{r} 125 \\ \times\ 19 \\ \hline 1125 \\ 125\ \ \\ \hline 2,375 \end{array}$$

4. (1) $2
$$\begin{array}{r} 2 \\ 8\overline{)16} \\ \underline{16} \end{array}$$

5. (3) $156
$$\begin{array}{r} 156 \\ 36\overline{)5616} \\ \underline{36}\ \ \ \\ 201 \\ \underline{180}\ \ \\ 216 \\ \underline{216} \end{array}$$

Page 29   Self-Test

6. (4) $4,208
$$\begin{array}{r} 263 \\ \times\ 16 \\ \hline 1578 \\ 263\ \ \\ \hline 4,208 \end{array}$$

7. (4) 40 weeks
$$\begin{array}{r} 40 \\ 25\overline{)1000} \\ \underline{100}\ \ \\ 00 \\ \underline{00} \end{array}$$

8. (5) 1,400 envelopes

$$
\begin{array}{r}
5\,0 \\
\times\ 2\,8 \\
\hline
4\,0\,0 \\
1\,0\,0 \\
\hline
1,4\,0\,0
\end{array}
$$

9. (2) 9 cases

$$
\begin{array}{r}
9 \\
24\overline{)216} \\
2\,1\,6
\end{array}
$$

10. (3) 15 gallons

$$
\begin{array}{r}
1\,5 \\
16\overline{)2\,4\,0} \\
1\,6 \\
\hline
8\,0 \\
8\,0
\end{array}
$$

Page 31 Practice

multiply; add; subtract;
Henry scored 4 more points

$$
\begin{array}{r}
1\,2 \\
\times\ \ 4 \\
\hline
4\,8
\end{array}
\qquad
\begin{array}{r}
1\,5 \\
1\,0 \\
5 \\
+\,1\,4 \\
\hline
4\,4
\end{array}
\qquad
\begin{array}{r}
4\,8 \\
-\,4\,4 \\
\hline
4
\end{array}
$$

Page 32 Self-Test

1. (2) 5 hr

$$
\begin{array}{r}
6 \\
4 \\
+\,3 \\
\hline
1\,3
\end{array}
\qquad
\begin{array}{r}
5 \\
+\,3 \\
\hline
8
\end{array}
\qquad
\begin{array}{r}
1\,3 \\
-\ 8 \\
\hline
5
\end{array}
$$

2. (2) 48

$$
\begin{array}{r}
4\,2 \\
4\,8 \\
4\,6 \\
5\,0 \\
+\,5\,4 \\
\hline
2\,4\,0
\end{array}
\qquad
\begin{array}{r}
4\,8 \\
5\overline{)2\,4\,0}
\end{array}
$$

3. (4) $312

$$
\begin{array}{r}
2\,0 \\
2\,2 \\
1\,8 \\
2\,3 \\
+\,2\,1 \\
\hline
1\,0\,4
\end{array}
\qquad
\begin{array}{r}
1\,0\,4 \\
\times\ \ \$3 \\
\hline
\$3\,1\,2
\end{array}
$$

4. (2) $304

$$
\begin{array}{r}
\$6\,0 \\
1\,2 \\
+\,2\,6 \\
\hline
\$9\,8
\end{array}
\qquad
\begin{array}{r}
\$4\,0\,2 \\
-\ \ 9\,8 \\
\hline
\$3\,0\,4
\end{array}
$$

5. (1) 68 in.

$$
\begin{array}{r}
1\,7 \\
\times\ 1\,0 \\
\hline
1\,7\,0
\end{array}
\qquad
\begin{array}{r}
1\,7\,0 \\
-\,1\,0\,2 \\
\hline
6\,8
\end{array}
$$

Page 33 Self-Test

6. (3) 180 lb

$$
\begin{array}{r}
2\,0\,0 \\
30\overline{)6\,0\,0\,0}
\end{array}
\qquad
\begin{array}{r}
2\,0\,0 \\
-\ \ 2\,0 \\
\hline
1\,8\,0
\end{array}
$$

7. (5) $226

$$
\begin{array}{r}
\$2\,0 \\
\times\ \ 4 \\
\hline
\$8\,0
\end{array}
\qquad
\begin{array}{r}
\$\ 8\,0 \\
1\,3\,5 \\
+\ \ 1\,1 \\
\hline
\$2\,2\,6
\end{array}
$$

8. (2) 200 miles

$$
\begin{array}{r}
1\,5\,0 \\
1\,5\,0 \\
+\,3\,0\,0 \\
\hline
6\,0\,0
\end{array}
\qquad
\begin{array}{r}
2\,0\,0 \\
3\overline{)6\,0\,0}
\end{array}
$$

9. (1) 2 ft

$$
\begin{array}{r}
3 \\
12\overline{)3\,6}
\end{array}
\qquad
\begin{array}{r}
5 \\
-\,3 \\
\hline
2
\end{array}
$$

10. (5) $225

$$
\begin{array}{r}
1\,8 \\
\times\ \ 3 \\
\hline
5\,4
\end{array}
\qquad
\begin{array}{r}
9 \\
6\overline{)5\,4}
\end{array}
\qquad
\begin{array}{r}
\$2\,5 \\
\times\ \ 9 \\
\hline
\$2\,2\,5
\end{array}
$$

Page 34 Self-Test

11. (5) 27,300 lb

$$
\begin{array}{r}
2\,6\,0 \\
\times\,1\,0\,5 \\
\hline
1\,3\,0\,0 \\
0\,0\,0 \\
2\,6\,0 \\
\hline
2\,7,3\,0\,0
\end{array}
$$

12. (3) 5 weeks

$$
\begin{array}{r}
\$1\,4\,5 \\
-\ \ 4\,5 \\
\hline
\$1\,0\,0
\end{array}
\qquad
\begin{array}{r}
5 \\
20\overline{)1\,0\,0}
\end{array}
$$

13. (4) 6 scarves

$$
\begin{array}{r}
\$3 \\
\times\,5 \\
\hline
\$1\,5
\end{array}
\quad
\begin{array}{r}
\$7 \\
\times\,7 \\
\hline
\$4\,9
\end{array}
\quad
\begin{array}{r}
\$1\,5 \\
+\,4\,9 \\
\hline
\$6\,4
\end{array}
\quad
\begin{array}{r}
\$9\,4 \\
-\,6\,4 \\
\hline
\$3\,0
\end{array}
\quad
\begin{array}{r}
6 \\
5\overline{)3\,0}
\end{array}
$$

14. (4) 232,500 qt

$$
\begin{array}{r}
7\,5\,0\,0 \\
\times\ \ \ 3\,1 \\
\hline
7\,5\,0\,0 \\
2\,2\,5\,0\,0 \\
\hline
2\,3\,2,5\,0\,0
\end{array}
$$

15. (1) 640 qt

$$
\begin{array}{r}
8\,7\,2 \\
\times\ \ \ 5 \\
\hline
4,3\,6\,0
\end{array}
\qquad
\begin{array}{r}
5,0\,0\,0 \\
-\,4,3\,6\,0 \\
\hline
6\,4\,0
\end{array}
$$

FRACTIONS

IN this unit, you will work with fractions. There will be some new rules for working with fractions. But you will use the skills you practiced in earlier units too. For example, when you solve the word problems in this unit, you will have to decide whether to add, subtract, multiply, or divide. Many of the problems will probably be familiar to you because you use fractions every day. You may have to cut a piece of wood $3\frac{1}{2}$ feet long for a bookshelf. Or you may make a recipe that calls for $\frac{3}{4}$ cup of milk.

1. FRACTIONS

Up to this point in the book, you have worked with whole numbers.   There are other numbers you use in everyday life.   They are called *fractions*.   For example, if you cut a piece of wood into two equal parts and take one part, you have taken one out of two pieces — *one-half.*

In numerals, *one-half* becomes $\frac{1}{2}$.   The figures below illustrate the number $\frac{1}{2}$.   Each figure has been cut into two equal parts, so 2 is the number under the line.   Each figure has one part shaded, so 1 is the number above the line.

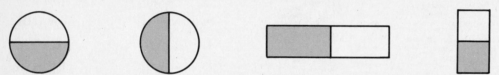

The fraction $\frac{1}{4}$ represents one out of four parts.   Each of the figures below shows $\frac{1}{4}$.

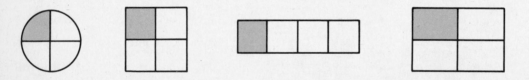

The bottom number of a fraction shows how many equal pieces make up the whole. The top number shows how many pieces you are talking about. The larger the number on the bottom, the smaller the parts compared to the whole. For example,

If the bottom number doesn't change and the top number gets larger, then you are refering to more of the whole. For example,

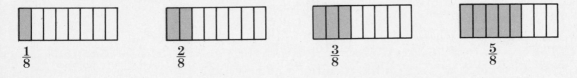

What if the numbers on the top and the bottom of the fraction are the same? Then you have a whole, or 1.

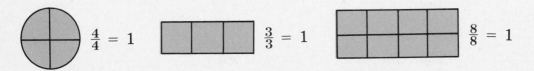

A place you see fractions marked is on a ruler. A ruler is marked off in inches. Each inch is divided into halves, quarters, fourths, eighths, and sixteenths of an inch.

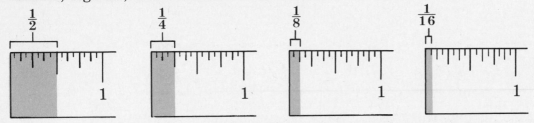

Practice. What part of each figure is shaded? Compare your answers with those in *Answers and Solutions* on page 61.

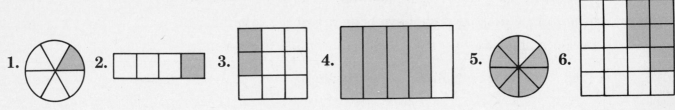

2. ADDING FRACTIONS

If you have $\frac{1}{3}$ cup of milk and add another $\frac{1}{3}$ cup, how much do you get? A picture of the situation looks like this:

$$\frac{1}{3} \quad + \quad \frac{1}{3} \quad = \quad \frac{2}{3}$$

If the bottom numbers are the same, you add the top numbers. The bottom number stays the same. The top number of a fraction is called the *numerator*. The bottom number is called the *denominator*.

$$\frac{numerator}{denominator}$$

Practice. Add these fractions. Then compare your answers with those in *Answers and Solutions* on page 61.

1. $\frac{7}{16}$ 2. $\frac{3}{5}$ 3. $\frac{2}{6}$ 4. $\frac{2}{10}$ 5. $\frac{3}{7}$ 6. $\frac{2}{8}$
$+ \frac{2}{16}$ $+ \frac{1}{5}$ $+ \frac{3}{6}$ $+ \frac{5}{10}$ $+ \frac{1}{7}$ $+ \frac{5}{8}$

Now look at this problem: $\frac{1}{4} + \frac{1}{2}$
To add $\frac{1}{4}$ and $\frac{1}{2}$ you must change the fractions so the denominators are the same. You do this by finding an *equivalent fraction*.

Equivalent fractions have the same value. For example, the squares at the top of the next page have been divided into halves. One-half has been shaded. Then each square divided further. In each case, $\frac{1}{2}$ of the square is shaded. $\frac{1}{2}, \frac{2}{4}, \frac{3}{6}, \frac{4}{8}$, and $\frac{8}{16}$ are all equivalent fractions.

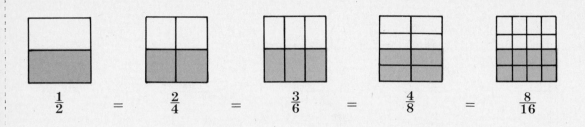

$$\frac{1}{2} \quad = \quad \frac{2}{4} \quad = \quad \frac{3}{6} \quad = \quad \frac{4}{8} \quad = \quad \frac{8}{16}$$

A fraction can be changed to an equivalent fraction by multiplying both the numerator and the denominator by the same number (not zero) or by dividing both the numerator and the denominator by the same number (not zero).

Examples:

$$\frac{2}{5} = \frac{2 \times 2}{5 \times 2} = \frac{4}{10} \qquad \frac{1}{6} = \frac{1 \times 5}{6 \times 5} = \frac{5}{30}$$

$$\frac{9}{12} = \frac{9 \div 3}{12 \div 3} = \frac{3}{4} \qquad \frac{10}{16} = \frac{10 \div 2}{16 \div 2} = \frac{5}{8}$$

Remember that any fraction which is the same on the top and the bottom is equivalent to 1.

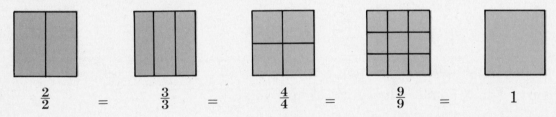

$$\frac{2}{2} \quad = \quad \frac{3}{3} \quad = \quad \frac{4}{4} \quad = \quad \frac{9}{9} \quad = \quad 1$$

Practice.   Look at each figure and find the equivalent fraction. The first one has been done for you.   Then compare your answers with those in *Answers and Solutions* on page 61.

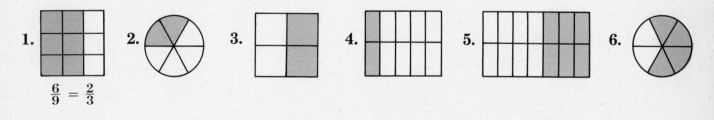

1. $\frac{6}{9} = \frac{2}{3}$ 2.   3.   4.   5.   6.

Look again at this problem: $\frac{1}{4} + \frac{1}{2}$

You must change at least one of the fractions so both denominators are the same.   To do this, use equivalent fractions.

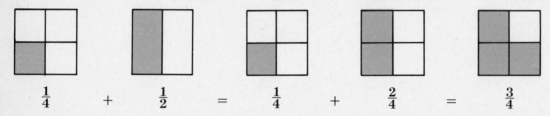

$$\frac{1}{4} \quad + \quad \frac{1}{2} \quad = \quad \frac{1}{4} \quad + \quad \frac{2}{4} \quad = \quad \frac{3}{4}$$

Practice.   Add these fractions.   Then compare your answers with those in *Answers and Solutions* on page 61.

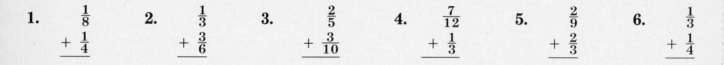

1. $\frac{1}{8}$ 2. $\frac{1}{3}$ 3. $\frac{2}{5}$ 4. $\frac{7}{12}$ 5. $\frac{2}{9}$ 6. $\frac{1}{3}$

$+ \frac{1}{4}$ $+ \frac{3}{6}$ $+ \frac{3}{10}$ $+ \frac{1}{3}$ $+ \frac{2}{3}$ $+ \frac{1}{4}$

You also use equivalent fractions to put answers into a *reduced form*.   Consider this example:

$$\frac{1}{6} \quad + \quad \frac{1}{6} \quad = \quad \frac{2}{6}$$

The sum $\frac{2}{6}$ is correct, but the equivalent fraction $\frac{1}{3}$ is simpler. $\frac{1}{3}$ is called the reduced form.   You should reduce a fraction if you can. If both the numerator and the denominator can be divided by the same number evenly, then the fraction can be reduced.

Example:

$$\frac{2}{6} \;=\; \frac{2 \div 2}{6 \div 2} = \frac{1}{3}$$

Practice.   Reduce these fractions.   Compare your answers with those in *Answers and Solutions* on page 61.

1. $\frac{3}{9}$ 2. $\frac{10}{15}$ 3. $\frac{2}{16}$ 4. $\frac{6}{12}$ 5. $\frac{6}{8}$ 6. $\frac{7}{21}$

Sometimes, after you add fractions, the numerator is larger than the denominator.   This means the sum is larger than 1.

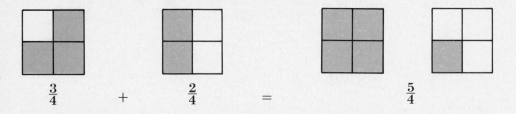

$$\frac{3}{4} \quad + \quad \frac{2}{4} \quad = \quad \frac{5}{4}$$

When this happens, change the fraction to a whole number and a fraction.   The result is called a *mixed number*.

Example:
$$\frac{3}{4} + \frac{2}{4} = \frac{5}{4} = \frac{4}{4} + \frac{1}{4} = 1 + \frac{1}{4} = 1\frac{1}{4}$$

To add mixed numbers, first add the fractions.   Then add the whole numbers.

Add fractions.   Add whole numbers.   Reduce if necessary.

$$
\begin{array}{c}
3\frac{1}{8} \\
+\,2\frac{5}{8} \\
\hline
\end{array}
\qquad
\begin{array}{c}
3\frac{1}{8} \\
+\,2\frac{5}{8} \\
\hline
\frac{6}{8}
\end{array}
\qquad
\begin{array}{c}
3\frac{1}{8} \\
+\,2\frac{5}{8} \\
\hline
5\frac{6}{8}
\end{array}
\quad = \quad 5\frac{3}{4}
$$

When you add mixed numbers, you may get a fraction larger than 1.   When this happens change the fraction to a mixed number.

Example:

$$
\begin{array}{c}
2\frac{3}{4} \\
+\,5\frac{5}{8} \\
\hline
\end{array}
\qquad
\begin{array}{c}
2\frac{6}{8} \\
+\,5\frac{5}{8} \\
\hline
7\frac{11}{8}
\end{array}
\quad = \quad 7 + 1\frac{3}{8} \quad = \quad 8\frac{3}{8}
$$

Practice.   Add.   Reduce if necessary.   Then compare your answers with those in *Answers and Solutions* on page 61.

1. $\quad 3\frac{2}{5}$ **2.** $\quad 6\frac{3}{8}$ **3.** $\quad 2\frac{3}{8}$ **4.** $\quad 3\frac{3}{4}$ **5.** $\quad 1\frac{1}{4}$ **6.** $\quad 4\frac{2}{3}$

$\quad\quad +\,4\frac{1}{5}$ $+\,1\frac{1}{4}$ $+\,3\frac{1}{8}$ $+\,2\frac{7}{8}$ $+\,5\frac{3}{4}$ $+\,1\frac{5}{6}$

STRATEGIES FOR SUCCESS

SOLVING PROBLEMS WITH A HIDDEN STEP

Sometimes there are hidden steps in a problem. For example, you may have to change the numbers or reduce.

STRATEGY 1: Think it through.

Read the problem several times. Think about what it says and what kind of answer it asks for.

Example: What kind of answer does this problem ask for? Is there a hidden step before you can do the operation?

In order to do a job, a plumber needs two pieces of pipe, one $5\frac{1}{8}$ in. long and one $10\frac{3}{16}$ in. long. What is the total length of the pipe he needs?

Read the problem carefully. *Total* is a key word. It tells you to add. Another word, *length*, tells you that your answer will be a measurement. Next, check for a hidden step. In this problem, the fractions have different denominators. You have to change to like denominators before you can add.

$$5 \ \frac{1}{8} \text{ in.} = \ \ \ 5 \ \frac{2}{16} \text{ in.}$$
$$+ \ 10 \ \frac{3}{16} \text{ in.} = \ + \ 10 \ \frac{3}{16} \text{ in.}$$
$$\overline{ 15 \ \frac{5}{16} \text{ in. of pipe}}$$

Solve this problem: Use Strategy 1.

Judy and Emilio ordered a pizza. Emilio ate $\frac{5}{8}$ of the pizza and Judy ate $\frac{1}{4}$. How much of the pizza did they eat in all?

- What's the operation? _____
- What's the hidden step? _____
- What's the answer? _____

STRATEGY 2:   Picture the situation.

Make a sketch to help you think through the problem.

Example: Is there a hidden step in this problem?

Alice and her daughter made
a paper bird.   They used $\frac{3}{8}$
sheet of paper for the body
and $\frac{5}{8}$ sheet for the wings.
How much paper did they use
altogether?

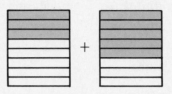

From the sketch, you can see that
you have two amounts to add.   The
numbers have like denominators.   So
there is no hidden step before the
operation.   After you add, check to see if
you can reduce your answer.   Reducing is
a hidden step.

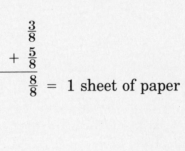

$$\begin{array}{r} \frac{3}{8} \\ +\ \frac{5}{8} \\ \hline \frac{8}{8} \end{array} = 1 \text{ sheet of paper}$$

Solve this problem.   Use Strategy 2.

Ralph took his three children to the movies.   During
the movie, May ate $1\frac{1}{2}$ candy bars, Sue ate $\frac{3}{4}$ candy bar,
and Reuben ate 2 candy bars.   How many candy bars
did they eat altogether?

- Draw a picture.
- What's the operation? _____
- What are the hidden steps? _____
- What's the answer? _____

Check your answers.   Read the problems again.   Make sure
you answered the questions.   Check your work for careless
errors.

Compare your answers with those in *Answers and Solutions* on page 61.

Self-Test

Solve these problems.   Put an X next to the correct answer.   Then compare your answers with those in *Answers and Solutions* on page 61.

Addition word problems with fractions.

1. Mrs. Frye is making a Halloween costume for her daughter.   She needs $\frac{1}{2}$ yard of green cloth and $\frac{1}{2}$ yard of yellow cloth.   How much cloth does she need altogether?

_____ (1) $\frac{1}{4}$ yd

_____ (2) $\frac{3}{4}$ yd

_____ (3) 1 yd

_____ (4) $1\frac{1}{2}$ yd

_____ (5) 2 yd

2. Hank wanted to do a load of laundry. He had only $\frac{1}{4}$ cup of laundry detergent. He borrowed $\frac{3}{4}$ cup from a neighbor. How much detergent did he then have to do his laundry?

_____ (1) $\frac{1}{8}$ cup

_____ (2) $\frac{1}{4}$ cup

_____ (3) $\frac{1}{2}$ cup

_____ (4) $\frac{3}{4}$ cup

_____ (5) 1 cup

3. Reggie bought $\frac{1}{2}$ lb of bread and $\frac{3}{4}$ lb of butter.   What was the total weight of his purchases?

_____ (1) $1\frac{1}{4}$ lb

_____ (2) $1\frac{1}{2}$ lb

_____ (3) $1\frac{3}{4}$ lb

_____ (4) $2\frac{3}{4}$ lb

_____ (5) 3 lb

4. Cindy's recipe calls for $1\frac{1}{3}$ cups of milk and $\frac{1}{3}$ cup of water.   How much liquid will there be when the two are put together?

_____ (1) 1 cup

_____ (2) $1\frac{2}{3}$ cups

_____ (3) $2\frac{1}{3}$ cups

_____ (4) $2\frac{2}{3}$ cups

_____ (5) 3 cups

5. Dolores Rios bought $1\frac{1}{6}$ lb of peanuts and $\frac{1}{6}$ lb of cashews to take to a party. What was the total weight of the nuts?

_____ (1) $\frac{1}{2}$ lb

_____ (2) $\frac{2}{3}$ lb

_____ (3) 1 lb

_____ (4) $1\frac{1}{3}$ lb

_____ (5) $1\frac{2}{3}$ lb

6. Mr. Sato put $1\frac{1}{4}$ cups of rice and $2\frac{1}{2}$ cups of water in a sauce pan. How many cups did he measure out altogether?

___ (1) $1\frac{1}{4}$ cups

___ (2) $1\frac{3}{4}$ cups

___ (3) 2 cups

___ (4) $3\frac{1}{4}$ cups

___ (5) $3\frac{3}{4}$ cups

7. Tim ate $\frac{1}{6}$ of a spinach pie. Rodney ate $\frac{1}{3}$ of the pie. How much of the pie did they eat?

___ (1) $\frac{1}{6}$

___ (2) $\frac{1}{3}$

___ (3) $\frac{1}{2}$

___ (4) $\frac{2}{3}$

___ (5) $\frac{5}{6}$

8. Ali bought $\frac{1}{2}$ pound of butter and $1\frac{1}{2}$ pounds of margarine. How much butter and margarine did he buy altogether?

___ (1) $\frac{3}{4}$ lb

___ (2) 1 lb

___ (3) $1\frac{1}{4}$ lb

___ (4) $1\frac{3}{4}$ lb

___ (5) 2 lb

9. In May it rained $1\frac{1}{4}$ inches and in June it rained $\frac{1}{2}$ inch. What was the total rainfall for May and June?

___ (1) $\frac{3}{8}$ in.

___ (2) $\frac{3}{4}$ in.

___ (3) $1\frac{3}{4}$ in.

___ (4) 2 in.

___ (5) $2\frac{3}{4}$ in.

10. Mrs. Glidden's baby weighed $6\frac{1}{2}$ lb when it was born. The baby has gained $2\frac{3}{8}$ lb. How much does the baby weigh?

___ (1) $8\frac{7}{8}$ lb

___ (2) $9\frac{1}{8}$ lb

___ (3) $8\frac{1}{2}$ lb

___ (4) $9\frac{3}{4}$ lb

___ (5) $9\frac{7}{8}$ lb

11. Jefferson has $2\frac{3}{4}$ quarts of oil in a storage can. If he adds $1\frac{1}{2}$ quarts of oil, how much will be in the storage can?

_____ (1) $3\frac{1}{4}$ qt

_____ (2) $3\frac{1}{2}$ qt

_____ (3) $3\frac{2}{3}$ qt

_____ (4) $4\frac{1}{4}$ qt

_____ (5) $4\frac{1}{3}$ qt

12. A soup recipe calls for $2\frac{3}{8}$ cups of diced carrots and $1\frac{3}{4}$ cups of chopped celery. What is the total amount of carrots and celery?

_____ (1) $3\frac{1}{4}$ cups

_____ (2) $3\frac{1}{2}$ cups

_____ (3) $4\frac{1}{8}$ cups

_____ (4) $4\frac{1}{4}$ cups

_____ (5) $4\frac{3}{8}$ cups

13. Al Gomez is mailing a toy truck to his grandson. The truck weighs $5\frac{2}{3}$ pounds and the box weighs $1\frac{1}{6}$ pounds. What is the total weight of the package?

_____ (1) $6\frac{1}{9}$ lb

_____ (2) $6\frac{1}{3}$ lb

_____ (3) $6\frac{1}{2}$ lb

_____ (4) $6\frac{2}{3}$ lb

_____ (5) $6\frac{5}{6}$ lb

14. Mrs. Huang is shopping for groceries. She buys 5 lb of potatoes, $1\frac{1}{2}$ lb of spinach, and $2\frac{3}{4}$ lb of onions. What is the total weight of her groceries?

_____ (1) $8\frac{1}{4}$ lb

_____ (2) $8\frac{3}{4}$ lb

_____ (3) 9 lb

_____ (4) $9\frac{1}{4}$ lb

_____ (5) $9\frac{1}{2}$ lb

15. Ms. Kelly has 3 pieces of drapery material. The pieces are $2\frac{5}{8}$ yd, $3\frac{1}{4}$ yd, and $1\frac{1}{2}$ yd long. How much material does she have altogether?

_____ (1) $6\frac{3}{8}$ yd

_____ (2) $7\frac{3}{8}$ yd

_____ (3) $7\frac{1}{2}$ yd

_____ (4) $7\frac{5}{8}$ yd

_____ (5) $7\frac{3}{4}$ yd

3. SUBTRACTING FRACTIONS

The rules for subtracting fractions are similar to the rules for adding fractions.

The denominator of the two fractions must be the same before you can subtract. If the denominators are different, find equivalent fractions to make them match.

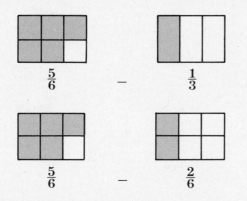

$$\frac{5}{6} \quad - \quad \frac{1}{3}$$

$$\frac{5}{6} \quad - \quad \frac{2}{6}$$

Subtract the numerators only. The denominators stay the same.

$$\frac{5}{6} - \frac{2}{6} = \frac{3}{6}$$

Reduce the answer if necessary.

$$\frac{3}{6} = \frac{1}{2}$$

If you have mixed numbers, subtract the fractions first. Then subtract the whole numbers.

	Subtract fractions.	Subtract whole numbers.
$14\frac{2}{3}$	$14\frac{2}{3}$	$14\frac{2}{3}$
$-\ 2\frac{1}{3}$	$-\ 2\frac{1}{3}$	$-\ 2\frac{1}{3}$
	$\frac{1}{3}$	$12\frac{1}{3}$

In the problem at the right, $\frac{3}{4}$ is larger than $\frac{1}{4}$.   So you must borrow.   To subtract $\frac{3}{4}$ from $\frac{1}{4}$, you borrow 1 from the whole number 3.

$$3\frac{1}{4}$$
$$-\ 2\frac{3}{4}$$

Borrow 1 from 3.
$$3\frac{1}{4} = 2 + 1\frac{1}{4} = 2 + \frac{4}{4} + \frac{1}{4} = 2\frac{5}{4}$$

$$2\frac{5}{4}$$
$$-\ 2\frac{3}{4}$$
$$\frac{2}{4} = \frac{1}{2}$$

Then reduce.

When you subtract a fraction from a whole number, you must borrow 1.

$$6 \qquad = \qquad 5 + 1 \qquad = \qquad 5 + \frac{3}{3} \qquad = \qquad 5\frac{3}{3}$$
$$-\ \frac{2}{3} \qquad\qquad\qquad\qquad\qquad\qquad\qquad\qquad\qquad\qquad -\ \frac{2}{3}$$
$$\qquad\qquad\qquad\qquad\qquad\qquad\qquad\qquad\qquad\qquad\qquad\qquad\qquad 5\frac{1}{3}$$

Practice.   Subtract.   Reduce if necessary.   Then compare your answers with those in *Answers and Solutions* on page 62.

1. $\frac{4}{5}$
    $-\ \frac{3}{5}$

2. $\frac{7}{10}$
    $-\ \frac{3}{10}$

3. $8\frac{3}{10}$
    $-\ 6\frac{1}{10}$

4. $13\frac{3}{4}$
    $-\ 7\frac{1}{2}$

5. $4\frac{1}{4}$
    $-\ 2\frac{3}{4}$

6. 9
    $-\ 3\frac{1}{5}$

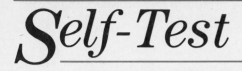

1. If $\frac{1}{3}$ yard of a plastic pipe is cut from a piece $\frac{2}{3}$ yard long, how much plastic pipe will be left?

____ (1) $\frac{1}{3}$ yd

____ (2) $\frac{2}{3}$ yd

____ (3) 1 yd

____ (4) $1\frac{1}{3}$ yd

____ (5) $1\frac{2}{3}$ yd

2. If a person does a job in $\frac{3}{4}$ of an hour, and a machine does the same job in $\frac{1}{4}$ of an hour, how much time does the machine save?

____ (1) $\frac{1}{4}$ hr

____ (2) $\frac{1}{2}$ hr

____ (3) $\frac{3}{4}$ hr

____ (4) 1 hr

____ (5) $1\frac{1}{4}$ hr

3. Angela had a piece of linoleum measuring $2\frac{3}{8}$ yards in length.   She cut off a piece $1\frac{1}{4}$ yards long.   How much linoleum did she have left?

____ (1) $\frac{7}{8}$ yd

____ (2) $1\frac{1}{8}$ yd

____ (3) $1\frac{1}{4}$ yd

____ (4) $1\frac{7}{8}$ yd

____ (5) $2\frac{1}{8}$ yd

4. Mr. Sample was building a tree house for his daughter.   He needed a board $2\frac{3}{4}$ feet long.   He had a 4-foot board.   How much wood was left over?

____ (1) $1\frac{1}{4}$ ft

____ (2) $1\frac{3}{4}$ ft

____ (3) $2\frac{1}{4}$ ft

____ (4) $2\frac{1}{2}$ ft

____ (5) $3\frac{1}{4}$ ft

5. Elena used $\frac{1}{5}$ of a can of paint to paint some bookshelves.   How much of the can of paint was left?

____ (1) $\frac{1}{10}$ can

____ (2) $\frac{1}{5}$ can

____ (3) $\frac{2}{5}$ can

____ (4) $\frac{4}{5}$ can

____ (5) $\frac{9}{10}$ can

Addition and subtraction problems. Remember to picture the situation clearly. Some problems require two steps.

6. On one day, Mobil Oil stock was selling for $30\frac{1}{4}$ points a share. On the next day, it was selling for $29\frac{3}{4}$ points. How many points did it drop?

—— (1) $\frac{1}{4}$ point

—— (2) $\frac{1}{2}$ point

—— (3) $1\frac{1}{4}$ points

—— (4) 2 points

—— (5) $2\frac{1}{2}$ points

7. George Simmons had a 5-pound box of grass seed. He used $\frac{3}{4}$ pound on his front lawn. He used $1\frac{7}{8}$ pounds on the side lawns. How much seed did he have left for the back lawn?

—— (1) $2\frac{3}{8}$ lb

—— (2) $2\frac{5}{8}$ lb

—— (3) $4\frac{1}{8}$ lb

—— (4) $4\frac{1}{4}$ lb

—— (5) $4\frac{7}{8}$ lb

8. Phil's pickup truck and car have the same size gas tank. If he takes the pickup truck to visit his parents, he uses $\frac{1}{2}$ tank of gas. If he takes the car he uses $\frac{3}{8}$ tank of gas. How much gas does he save by using the car?

—— (1) $\frac{1}{8}$ tank

—— (2) $\frac{1}{4}$ tank

—— (3) $\frac{3}{8}$ tank

—— (4) $\frac{3}{4}$ tank

—— (5) $1\frac{1}{8}$ tank

9. In one month, Jean spent $\frac{1}{3}$ of her money on rent and $\frac{1}{6}$ of her money on groceries. What fraction of her money did she have left?

—— (1) $\frac{1}{6}$

—— (2) $\frac{1}{3}$

—— (3) $\frac{1}{2}$

—— (4) $\frac{2}{3}$

—— (5) $\frac{5}{6}$

10. Shirley Curtis shops for groceries on her way home from work. She spends $\frac{2}{5}$ of an hour in the grocery store and then $\frac{9}{10}$ of an hour cooking dinner. How much time does she spend shopping and cooking?

—— (1) $\frac{1}{2}$ hr

—— (2) $\frac{7}{10}$ hr

—— (3) $1\frac{1}{5}$ hr

—— (4) $1\frac{4}{15}$ hr

—— (5) $1\frac{3}{10}$ hr

4. MULTIPLYING FRACTIONS

This section will show you how to multiply fractions. Look at this problem:

What is $\frac{1}{3} \times \frac{1}{2}$?

Instead of saying "times" you can say "of." In other words, what is $\frac{1}{3}$ of $\frac{1}{2}$? First picture the problem.

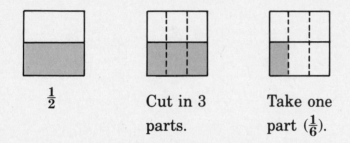

$\frac{1}{2}$ Cut in 3 parts.   Take one part ($\frac{1}{6}$).

To find $\frac{1}{3} \times \frac{1}{2}$ without drawing a picture, use this rule:

Multiply the numerators and multiply the denominators. $\frac{1}{2} \times \frac{1}{3} = \frac{1 \times 1}{2 \times 3} = \frac{1}{6}$

To multiply a fraction and a whole number, consider this example:

What is $\frac{1}{2} \times 6$?

First the whole number must be written as a fraction. Any whole number can be written as a fraction. Just write the whole number over 1, for example $6 = \frac{6}{1}$.

Multiply the numerators and multiply the denominators. $\frac{1}{2} \times \frac{6}{1} = \frac{1 \times 6}{2 \times 1} = \frac{6}{2}$

Reduce if possible. $\frac{6}{2} = \frac{6 \div 2}{2 \div 2} = \frac{3}{1} = 3$

To multiply a fraction and a mixed number, consider this example:

What is $\frac{1}{3} \times 4\frac{1}{2}$?

First the mixed number must be written as a fraction.

$$4\frac{1}{2} = \frac{9}{2}$$

To change a mixed number to a fraction, multiply the whole number times the denominator of the fraction.

$$4 \times 2 = 8$$

Then add the numerator.

$$8 + 1 = 9$$

Put the answer over the denominator.

$$\frac{9}{2}$$

Now multiply the numerators and multiply the denominators.

$$\frac{1}{3} \times \frac{9}{2} = \frac{1 \times 9}{3 \times 2} = \frac{9}{6}$$

Reduce if possible.

$$\frac{9}{6} = \frac{9 \div 3}{6 \div 3} = \frac{3}{2} = 1\frac{1}{2}$$

Practice. Multiply. Then compare your answers with those in *Answers and Solutions* on page 63.

1. $\frac{1}{2} \times \frac{1}{5}$ 2. $\frac{2}{3} \times \frac{1}{4}$ 3. $\frac{3}{4} \times \frac{1}{5}$

4. $\frac{1}{2} \times 8$ 5. $\frac{1}{2} \times 5$ 6. $\frac{2}{3} \times 1\frac{1}{2}$

7. $\frac{1}{5} \times 3\frac{1}{3}$ 8. $\frac{3}{4} \times 2\frac{2}{3}$ 9. $\frac{1}{8} \times \frac{2}{3}$

10. $1\frac{2}{3} \times \frac{1}{5}$ 11. $6 \times \frac{2}{3}$ 12. $\frac{5}{6} \times 2\frac{2}{5}$

Self-Test

Multiplication word problems with fractions.

1. Henry works part time and takes home $120 in pay each week. He saves $\frac{1}{4}$ of this amount. How much does he save each week?
   - _____ (1) $3
   - _____ (2) $12
   - _____ (3) $30
   - _____ (4) $48
   - _____ (5) $480

2. At the beginning of the week, the Recycle Co. had $\frac{1}{3}$ of a ton of aluminum. During the week, they sold $\frac{3}{4}$ of the aluminum. How many tons were sold?
   - _____ (1) $\frac{1}{4}$ ton
   - _____ (2) $\frac{4}{9}$ ton
   - _____ (3) $1\frac{3}{4}$ tons
   - _____ (4) $3\frac{3}{4}$ tons
   - _____ (5) 4 tons

3. Emily had $3\frac{1}{3}$ pounds of raspberries. She gave $\frac{1}{4}$ of them to her brother. How much did Emily give to her brother?
   - _____ (1) $\frac{1}{3}$ lb
   - _____ (2) $\frac{5}{6}$ lb
   - _____ (3) $2\frac{1}{3}$ lb
   - _____ (4) $2\frac{1}{2}$ lb
   - _____ (5) 3 lb

4. To mix the shade of green he wants, Mr. Heathcliff must add blue paint equal to $\frac{1}{6}$ of the amount of yellow paint. If he uses $4\frac{1}{2}$ gallons of yellow paint, how much blue paint does he need?
   - _____ (1) $\frac{1}{3}$ gallon
   - _____ (2) $\frac{3}{4}$ gallon
   - _____ (3) $1\frac{1}{2}$ gallons
   - _____ (4) $1\frac{3}{4}$ gallons
   - _____ (5) 12 gallons

5. Mrs. Farrell walks every day for exercise. She can walk at a rate of $3\frac{3}{4}$ miles per hour. How far can she walk in $\frac{1}{3}$ of an hour?
   - _____ (1) $\frac{7}{12}$ mi
   - _____ (2) $\frac{3}{4}$ mi
   - _____ (3) 1 mi
   - _____ (4) $1\frac{1}{4}$ mi
   - _____ (5) $1\frac{1}{2}$ mi

Addition, subtraction, and multiplication problems. Some of the problems require two steps. Remember to picture the situation clearly.

6. Before making dinner, Neil had $2\frac{1}{4}$ cups of shrimp. He used $\frac{2}{3}$ of the shrimp in his main dish. How much shrimp did he use?

    _____ (1) $\frac{1}{2}$ cup

    _____ (2) $\frac{3}{4}$ cup

    _____ (3) $\frac{2}{3}$ cup

    _____ (4) $1\frac{1}{4}$ cups

    _____ (5) $1\frac{1}{2}$ cups

7. Angela makes costume jewelry. At the beginning of one day, she had about $6\frac{1}{3}$ bags of beads. She used one bag before lunch. After lunch, she used half of what was left. How many bags did she have at the end of the day?

    _____ (1) $2\frac{1}{6}$ bags

    _____ (2) $2\frac{1}{3}$ bags

    _____ (3) $2\frac{2}{3}$ bags

    _____ (4) $3\frac{1}{6}$ bags

    _____ (5) $3\frac{1}{3}$ bags

8. Mr. Ono was framing a picture. He had $6\frac{1}{4}$ feet of wood. He used $\frac{4}{5}$ of it on one frame. How many feet did he have left?

    _____ (1) $1\frac{1}{4}$ ft

    _____ (2) 2 ft

    _____ (3) $2\frac{1}{4}$ ft

    _____ (4) $4\frac{4}{5}$ ft

    _____ (5) 5 ft

9. Ms. MacKenzie spent $3\frac{1}{5}$ hours moving lumber. $\frac{1}{4}$ of the time was spent driving the truck. The rest of the time was spent loading and unloading the truck. How much time was spent loading and unloading the truck?

    _____ (1) $1\frac{1}{5}$ hr

    _____ (2) $1\frac{3}{5}$ hr

    _____ (3) $2\frac{1}{5}$ hr

    _____ (4) $2\frac{2}{5}$ hr

    _____ (5) $2\frac{4}{5}$ hr

10. Mr. Rios bought a microwave oven for $231. He paid $\frac{1}{3}$ down on Tuesday. He paid the rest when he picked it up on Saturday. How much did he pay on Saturday?

    _____ (1) $77

    _____ (2) $82

    _____ (3) $94

    _____ (4) $135

    _____ (5) $154

5. DIVIDING FRACTIONS

Look at this division problem.

What is $\frac{1}{2} \div \frac{1}{4}$?

This problem asks how many $\frac{1}{4}$'s there are in $\frac{1}{2}$.

$\frac{1}{2}$ two $\frac{1}{4}$'s

There are two $\frac{1}{4}$'s in $\frac{1}{2}$. So $\frac{1}{2} \div \frac{1}{4} = 2$. Here are the rules for dividing with fractions.

Write both numbers as fractions. $\frac{1}{2} \div \frac{1}{4}$

Invert the second fraction and change to multiplication. $\frac{1}{2} \times \frac{4}{1}$

Multiply the numerators and multiply the denominators. $\frac{1 \times 4}{2 \times 1} = \frac{4}{2}$

Reduce if possible. $\frac{4}{2} = 2$

Practice. Divide. Then compare your answers with those in *Answers and Solutions* on page 63.

1. $\frac{1}{3} \div \frac{1}{6}$ 2. $\frac{3}{5} \div \frac{1}{5}$ 3. $\frac{1}{8} \div \frac{3}{4}$

4. $\frac{2}{3} \div \frac{1}{4}$ 5. $\frac{3}{4} \div \frac{1}{5}$ 6. $\frac{2}{5} \div \frac{2}{7}$

Now look at this problem.   What is $3\frac{1}{5} \div 1\frac{1}{5}$?

Write both numbers as fractions. $3\frac{1}{5} \div 1\frac{1}{5} = \frac{16}{5} \div \frac{6}{5}$

Invert the second number and change to multiplication. $\frac{16}{5} \times \frac{5}{6}$

Multiply the numerators and multiply the denominators. $\frac{16 \times 5}{5 \times 6} = \frac{80}{30}$

Reduce if possible. $\frac{80}{30} = \frac{80 \div 10}{30 \div 10} = \frac{8}{3} = 2\frac{2}{3}$

FOR YOUR INFORMATION

Here is a way to reduce.   It is called *canceling*.   It is useful when multiplying or dividing fractions.

Look to see if one numerator and one denominator can be divided by the same number.

$$\frac{16 \times 5}{5 \times 6}$$

You can divide both the numerator and the denominator by 5.   The 5's can be canceled since $5 \div 5 = 1$.   Cross out each 5 and write 1.

$$\frac{16 \times \overset{1}{\cancel{5}}}{\underset{1}{\cancel{5}} \times 6}$$

Look again.   16 and 6 can be canceled too. $16 \div 2 = 8$ and $6 \div 2 = 3$.   Cross out 16 and write 8. Cross out 6 and write 3.

$$\frac{\overset{8}{\cancel{16}} \times \overset{1}{\cancel{5}}}{\underset{1}{\cancel{5}} \times \underset{3}{\cancel{6}}}$$

Now multiply the new numbers.   By canceling you may not have to reduce later on.

$$\frac{\overset{8}{\cancel{16}} \times \overset{1}{\cancel{5}}}{\underset{1}{\cancel{5}} \times \underset{3}{\cancel{6}}} = \frac{8}{3} = 2\frac{2}{3}$$

Practice.   Divide.   Then compare your answers with those in *Answers and Solutions* on page 63.

1. $\frac{4}{5} \div 2$ 2. $3\frac{3}{4} \div \frac{1}{2}$ 3. $6 \div 3\frac{1}{3}$ 4. $2\frac{1}{4} \div 1\frac{1}{3}$ 5. $2\frac{1}{8} \div 2\frac{1}{8}$ 6. $1\frac{2}{5} \div 3\frac{1}{4}$

Division word problems with fractions.

1. Inez makes small wooden boxes for her friends.   She has a strip of wood $1\frac{3}{4}$ inches long.   How many $\frac{1}{4}$-inch strips can she cut from the $1\frac{3}{4}$-inch strip?

   _____ (1) $\frac{7}{8}$ strips

   _____ (2) 2 strips

   _____ (3) 3 strips

   _____ (4) 4 strips

   _____ (5) 7 strips

2. A recipe for chili calls for $1\frac{1}{3}$ cups of tomatoes.   How many recipes could be made from $3\frac{1}{3}$ cups of tomatoes?

   _____ (1) $1\frac{1}{2}$ recipes

   _____ (2) $2\frac{1}{2}$ recipes

   _____ (3) 3 recipes

   _____ (4) $3\frac{1}{2}$ recipes

   _____ (5) 4 recipes

3. Franklin packs oranges into bags. Each bag holds $2\frac{1}{2}$ pounds of oranges. How many bags can Franklin fill from a crate that holds 25 pounds?

   _____ (1) 8 bags

   _____ (2) 10 bags

   _____ (3) 12 bags

   _____ (4) 13 bags

   _____ (5) 15 bags

4. Mr. Lincoln is a tailor.   It takes him about half an hour to do an alteration in his shop.   How many alterations could he do in $3\frac{3}{4}$ hours?

   _____ (1) 3 alternations

   _____ (2) 6 alterations

   _____ (3) $6\frac{1}{2}$ alterations

   _____ (4) $7\frac{1}{2}$ alterations

   _____ (5) 9 alterations

5. Cass Crain is a bus driver.   One round trip on her route takes $1\frac{1}{3}$ hours.   How many round trips does she make if she works 8 hours?

   _____ (1) $4\frac{1}{2}$ trips

   _____ (2) 6 trips

   _____ (3) 7 trips

   _____ (4) $7\frac{1}{2}$ trips

   _____ (5) 8 trips

6. Mrs. Wong bought $3\frac{1}{3}$ pounds of fish for dinner. She divided it into 5 equal servings. How much did each serving weigh?

_____ (1) $\frac{2}{3}$ lb

_____ (2) $\frac{11}{15}$ lb

_____ (3) $\frac{3}{4}$ lb

_____ (4) $1\frac{1}{3}$ lb

_____ (5) $1\frac{1}{2}$ lb

7. A grocer divided a $4\frac{1}{2}$-pound piece of cheese into smaller pieces that weighed $\frac{3}{4}$ pound each. How many pieces did he get?

_____ (1) 3 pieces

_____ (2) $3\frac{3}{4}$ pieces

_____ (3) $4\frac{1}{4}$ pieces

_____ (4) 6 pieces

_____ (5) 8 pieces

8. Mr. Marsh built a fence. He cut some posts from a piece of pipe $4\frac{2}{3}$ yd long. Each post was $1\frac{1}{3}$ yd long. How many posts could be made from the piece of pipe?

_____ (1) $2\frac{2}{3}$ posts

_____ (2) $3\frac{1}{3}$ posts

_____ (3) $3\frac{1}{2}$ posts

_____ (4) 4 posts

_____ (5) $4\frac{1}{2}$ posts

9. Al Walters bought $\frac{3}{4}$ of a ton of bricks to build a wall around his patio. He can only carry $\frac{1}{8}$ of a ton in his pickup truck. How many trips must he make to get the bricks home?

_____ (1) 2 trips

_____ (2) 3 trips

_____ (3) 4 trips

_____ (4) 5 trips

_____ (5) 6 trips

10. The New Town Development Corporation has $8\frac{1}{3}$ acres of land. They plan to build 20 houses on the land. All the houses are to be built on plots of the same size. How large will each plot be?

_____ (1) $\frac{5}{12}$ acre

_____ (2) $\frac{1}{2}$ acre

_____ (3) $\frac{2}{3}$ acres

_____ (4) $1\frac{3}{4}$ acres

_____ (5) $2\frac{2}{5}$ acres

Answers and Solutions

1. $\frac{1}{6}$ 2. $\frac{1}{4}$ 3. $\frac{2}{9}$
4. $\frac{4}{5}$ 5. $\frac{7}{8}$ 6. $\frac{5}{16}$

Page 40   Practice
1. $\frac{9}{16}$ 2. $\frac{4}{5}$ 3. $\frac{5}{6}$
4. $\frac{7}{10}$ 5. $\frac{4}{7}$ 6. $\frac{7}{8}$

Page 41   Practice
1. $\frac{6}{9} = \frac{2}{3}$ 2. $\frac{2}{6} = \frac{1}{3}$ 3. $\frac{2}{4} = \frac{1}{2}$
4. $\frac{2}{10} = \frac{1}{5}$ 5. $\frac{6}{14} = \frac{3}{7}$ 6. $\frac{4}{6} = \frac{2}{3}$

Page 42   Practice

1.
$$\begin{array}{r} \frac{1}{8} = \frac{1}{8} \\ + \frac{1}{4} = \frac{2}{8} \\ \hline \frac{3}{8} \end{array}$$

2.
$$\begin{array}{r} \frac{1}{3} = \frac{2}{6} \\ + \frac{3}{6} = \frac{3}{6} \\ \hline \frac{5}{6} \end{array}$$

3.
$$\begin{array}{r} \frac{2}{5} = \frac{4}{10} \\ + \frac{3}{10} = \frac{3}{10} \\ \hline \frac{7}{10} \end{array}$$

4.
$$\begin{array}{r} \frac{7}{12} = \frac{7}{12} \\ + \frac{1}{3} = \frac{4}{12} \\ \hline \frac{11}{12} \end{array}$$

5.
$$\begin{array}{r} \frac{2}{9} = \frac{2}{9} \\ + \frac{2}{3} = \frac{6}{9} \\ \hline \frac{8}{9} \end{array}$$

6.
$$\begin{array}{r} \frac{1}{3} = \frac{4}{12} \\ + \frac{1}{4} = \frac{3}{12} \\ \hline \frac{7}{12} \end{array}$$

Page 42   Practice
1. $\frac{3}{9} = \frac{3 \div 3}{9 \div 3} = \frac{1}{3}$ 4. $\frac{6}{12} = \frac{6 \div 6}{12 \div 6} = \frac{1}{2}$

2. $\frac{10}{15} = \frac{10 \div 5}{15 \div 5} = \frac{2}{3}$ 5. $\frac{6}{8} = \frac{6 \div 2}{8 \div 2} = \frac{3}{4}$

3. $\frac{2}{16} = \frac{2 \div 2}{16 \div 2} = \frac{1}{8}$ 6. $\frac{7}{21} = \frac{7 \div 7}{21 \div 7} = \frac{1}{3}$

Page 43   Practice

1.
$$\begin{array}{r} 3\frac{2}{5} \\ + 4\frac{1}{5} \\ \hline 7\frac{3}{5} \end{array}$$

2.
$$\begin{array}{r} 6\frac{3}{8} = 6\frac{3}{8} \\ + 1\frac{1}{4} = 1\frac{2}{8} \\ \hline 7\frac{5}{8} \end{array}$$

3.
$$\begin{array}{r} 2\frac{3}{8} \\ + 3\frac{1}{8} \\ \hline 5\frac{4}{8} = 5\frac{1}{2} \end{array}$$

4.
$$\begin{array}{r} 3\frac{3}{4} = 3\frac{6}{8} \\ + 2\frac{7}{8} = 2\frac{7}{8} \\ \hline 5\frac{13}{8} = 6\frac{5}{8} \end{array}$$

5.
$$\begin{array}{r} 1\frac{1}{4} \\ + 5\frac{3}{4} \\ \hline 6\frac{4}{4} = 7 \end{array}$$

6.
$$\begin{array}{r} 4\frac{2}{3} = 4\frac{4}{6} \\ + 1\frac{5}{6} = 1\frac{5}{6} \\ \hline 5\frac{9}{6} = 6\frac{3}{6} \\ = 6\frac{1}{2} \end{array}$$

Page 44   Strategies For Success
- addition
- change to like denominators
- $\frac{7}{8}$ of the pizza was eaten

$$\begin{array}{r} \frac{5}{8} = \frac{5}{8} \\ + \frac{1}{4} = \frac{2}{8} \\ \hline \frac{7}{8} \end{array}$$

Page 45   Strategies For Success

$1\frac{1}{2}$ $\frac{3}{4}$ 2

$$\begin{array}{r} 1\frac{1}{2} = 1\frac{2}{4} \\ \frac{3}{4} = \frac{3}{4} \\ + 2 = 2 \\ \hline 3\frac{5}{4} = 4\frac{1}{4} \end{array}$$

- addition
- change to like denominators and change the answer
- $4\frac{1}{4}$ candy bars were eaten

Page 46   Self-Test
1. (3) 1 yd
$$\begin{array}{r} \frac{1}{2} \\ + \frac{1}{2} \\ \hline \frac{2}{2} = 1 \end{array}$$

2. (5) 1 cup
$$\begin{array}{r} \frac{1}{4} \\ + \frac{3}{4} \\ \hline \frac{4}{4} = 1 \end{array}$$

3. (1) $1\frac{1}{4}$ lb
$$\begin{array}{r} \frac{1}{2} = \frac{2}{4} \\ + \frac{3}{4} = \frac{3}{4} \\ \hline \frac{5}{4} = 1\frac{1}{4} \end{array}$$

4. (2) $1\frac{2}{3}$ cups
$$\begin{array}{r} 1\frac{1}{3} \\ + \frac{1}{3} \\ \hline 1\frac{2}{3} \end{array}$$

5. (4) $1\frac{1}{3}$ lb
$$\begin{array}{r} 1\frac{1}{6} \\ + \frac{1}{6} \\ \hline 1\frac{2}{6} = 1\frac{1}{3} \end{array}$$

Page 47   Self-Test
6. (5) $3\frac{3}{4}$ cups
$$\begin{array}{r} 1\frac{1}{4} = 1\frac{1}{4} \\ + 2\frac{1}{2} = 2\frac{2}{4} \\ \hline 3\frac{3}{4} \end{array}$$

7. (3) $\frac{1}{2}$

$$\frac{1}{6} = \frac{1}{6}$$
$$+ \frac{1}{3} = \frac{2}{6}$$
$$\frac{3}{6} = \frac{1}{2}$$

8. (5) 2 lb

$$\frac{1}{2}$$
$$+ 1\frac{1}{2}$$
$$1\frac{2}{2} = 1 + 1 = 2$$

9. (3) $1\frac{3}{4}$ in.

$$1\frac{1}{4} = 1\frac{1}{4}$$
$$+ \frac{1}{2} = \frac{2}{4}$$
$$1\frac{3}{4}$$

10. (1) $8\frac{7}{8}$ lb

$$6\frac{1}{2} = 6\frac{4}{8}$$
$$+ 2\frac{3}{8} = 2\frac{3}{8}$$
$$8\frac{7}{8}$$

Page 48   Self-Test

11. (4) $4\frac{1}{4}$ qt

$$2\frac{3}{4} = 2\frac{3}{4}$$
$$+ 1\frac{1}{2} = 1\frac{2}{4}$$
$$3\frac{5}{4} = 4\frac{1}{4}$$

12. (3) $4\frac{1}{8}$ cups

$$2\frac{3}{8} = 2\frac{3}{8}$$
$$+ 1\frac{3}{4} = 1\frac{6}{8}$$
$$3\frac{9}{8} = 4\frac{1}{8}$$

13. (5) $6\frac{5}{6}$ lb

$$5\frac{2}{3} = 5\frac{4}{6}$$
$$+ 1\frac{1}{6} = 1\frac{1}{6}$$
$$6\frac{5}{6}$$

14. (4) $9\frac{1}{4}$ lb

$$5 = 5$$
$$1\frac{1}{2} = 1\frac{2}{4}$$
$$+ 2\frac{3}{4} = 2\frac{3}{4}$$
$$8\frac{5}{4} = 9\frac{1}{4}$$

15. (2) $7\frac{3}{8}$ yd

$$2\frac{5}{8} = 2\frac{5}{8}$$
$$3\frac{1}{4} = 3\frac{2}{8}$$
$$+ 1\frac{1}{2} = 1\frac{4}{8}$$
$$6\frac{11}{8} = 7\frac{3}{8}$$

Page 50   Practice

1. $\frac{1}{5}$ **2.** $\frac{4}{10} = \frac{2}{5}$ **3.** $2\frac{2}{10} = 2\frac{1}{5}$

4.
$$13\frac{3}{4} = 13\frac{3}{4}$$
$$- 7\frac{1}{2} = 7\frac{2}{4}$$
$$6\frac{1}{4}$$

5.
$$4\frac{1}{4} = 3\frac{5}{4}$$
$$- 2\frac{3}{4} = 2\frac{3}{4}$$
$$1\frac{2}{4} = 1\frac{1}{2}$$

6.
$$9 = 8\frac{5}{5}$$
$$- 3\frac{1}{5} = 3\frac{1}{5}$$
$$5\frac{4}{5}$$

Page 51   Self-Test

1. (1) $\frac{1}{3}$ yd

$$\frac{2}{3}$$
$$- \frac{1}{3}$$
$$\frac{1}{3}$$

2. (2) $\frac{1}{2}$ hr

$$\frac{3}{4}$$
$$- \frac{1}{4}$$
$$\frac{2}{4} = \frac{1}{2}$$

3. (2) $1\frac{1}{8}$ yd

$$2\frac{3}{8} = 2\frac{3}{8}$$
$$- 1\frac{1}{4} = 1\frac{2}{8}$$
$$1\frac{1}{8}$$

4. (1) $1\frac{1}{4}$ ft

$$4 = 3\frac{4}{4}$$
$$- 2\frac{3}{4} = 2\frac{3}{4}$$
$$1\frac{1}{4}$$

5. (4) $\frac{4}{5}$ can

$$1 = \frac{5}{5}$$
$$- \frac{1}{5} = \frac{1}{5}$$
$$\frac{4}{5}$$

Page 52   Self-Test

6. (2) $\frac{1}{2}$ point

$$30\frac{1}{4} = 29\frac{5}{4}$$
$$- 29\frac{3}{4} = 29\frac{3}{4}$$
$$\frac{2}{4} = \frac{1}{2}$$

7. (1) $2\frac{3}{8}$ lb

$$\frac{3}{4} = \frac{6}{8}$$
$$+ 1\frac{7}{8} = 1\frac{7}{8}$$
$$1\frac{13}{8} = 2\frac{5}{8}$$

$$5 = 4\frac{8}{8}$$
$$- 2\frac{5}{8} = 2\frac{5}{8}$$
$$2\frac{3}{8}$$

8. (1) $\frac{1}{8}$ tank

$$\frac{1}{2} = \frac{4}{8}$$
$$- \frac{3}{8} = \frac{3}{8}$$
$$\frac{1}{8}$$

9. (3) $\frac{1}{2}$

$$\frac{1}{3} = \frac{2}{6}$$
$$+ \frac{1}{6} = \frac{1}{6}$$
$$\frac{3}{6} = \frac{1}{2}$$

$$1$$
$$- \frac{1}{2}$$
$$\frac{1}{2}$$

10. (5) $1\frac{3}{10}$ hr

$$\frac{2}{5} = \frac{4}{10}$$
$$+ \frac{9}{10} = \frac{9}{10}$$
$$\frac{13}{10} = 1\frac{3}{10}$$

Page 54   Practice

1. $\frac{1}{10}$

2. $\frac{2}{12} = \frac{1}{6}$

3. $\frac{3}{20}$

4. $\frac{1}{2} \times \frac{8}{1} = \frac{8}{2} = 4$

5. $\frac{1}{2} \times \frac{5}{1} = \frac{5}{2} = 2\frac{1}{2}$

6. $\frac{2}{3} \times \frac{3}{2} = \frac{6}{6} = 1$

7. $\frac{1}{5} \times \frac{10}{3} = \frac{10}{15} = \frac{2}{3}$

8. $\frac{3}{4} \times \frac{8}{3} = \frac{24}{12} = 2$

9. $\frac{2}{24} = \frac{1}{12}$

10. $\frac{5}{3} \times \frac{1}{5} = \frac{5}{15} = \frac{1}{3}$

11. $\frac{6}{1} \times \frac{2}{3} = \frac{12}{3} = 4$

12. $\frac{5}{6} \times \frac{12}{5} = \frac{60}{30} = 2$

Page 55   Self-Test

1. (3) $30

$$\frac{1}{4} \times 120 = \frac{1}{4} \times \frac{120}{1} = \frac{120}{4} = 30$$

2. (1) $\frac{1}{4}$ ton

$$\frac{1}{3} \times \frac{3}{4} = \frac{3}{12} = \frac{1}{4}$$

3. (2) $\frac{5}{6}$ lb

$$\frac{1}{4} \times 3\frac{1}{3} = \frac{1}{4} \times \frac{10}{3} = \frac{10}{12} = \frac{5}{6}$$

4. (2) $\frac{3}{4}$ gallon

$$\frac{1}{6} \times 4\frac{1}{2} = \frac{1}{6} \times \frac{9}{2} = \frac{9}{12} = \frac{3}{4}$$

5. (4) $1\frac{1}{4}$ mi

$$\frac{1}{3} \times 3\frac{3}{4} = \frac{1}{3} \times \frac{15}{4} = \frac{15}{12} = \frac{5}{4} = 1\frac{1}{4}$$

Page 56   Self-Test

6. (5) $1\frac{1}{2}$ cups

$$\frac{2}{3} \times 2\frac{1}{4} = \frac{2}{3} \times \frac{9}{4}$$
$$= \frac{18}{12} = \frac{3}{2} = 1\frac{1}{2}$$

7. (3) $2\frac{2}{3}$ bags

$$6\frac{1}{3}$$
$$- 1$$
$$5\frac{1}{3}$$

$$\frac{1}{2} \times 5\frac{1}{3} = \frac{1}{2} \times \frac{16}{3}$$
$$= \frac{16}{6} = \frac{8}{3} = 2\frac{2}{3}$$

8. (1) $1\frac{1}{4}$ ft

$$\frac{4}{5} \times 6\frac{1}{4} = \frac{4}{5} \times \frac{25}{4}$$
$$= \frac{100}{20} = 5$$

$$6\frac{1}{4}$$
$$- 5$$
$$1\frac{1}{4}$$

9. (4) $2\frac{2}{5}$ hr

$$\frac{1}{4} \times 3\frac{1}{5} = \frac{1}{4} \times \frac{16}{5}$$
$$= \frac{16}{20} = \frac{4}{5}$$

$$3\frac{1}{5} = 2\frac{6}{5}$$
$$- \frac{4}{5} = \frac{4}{5}$$
$$2\frac{2}{5}$$

10. (5) $154

$$\frac{1}{3} \times 231 = \frac{1}{3} \times \frac{231}{1}$$
$$= \frac{231}{3} = 77$$

$$\$2\,3\,1$$
$$- \quad 7\,7$$
$$\$1\,5\,4$$

Page 57   Practice

1. $\frac{1}{3} \div \frac{1}{6} = \frac{1}{3} \times \frac{6}{1} = \frac{6}{3} = 2$

2. $\frac{3}{5} \div \frac{1}{5} = \frac{3}{5} \times \frac{5}{1} = \frac{15}{5} = 3$

3. $\frac{1}{8} \div \frac{3}{4} = \frac{1}{8} \times \frac{4}{3} = \frac{4}{24} = \frac{1}{6}$

4. $\frac{2}{3} \div \frac{1}{4} = \frac{2}{3} \times \frac{4}{1} = \frac{8}{3} = 2\frac{2}{3}$

5. $\frac{3}{4} \div \frac{1}{5} = \frac{3}{4} \times \frac{5}{1} = \frac{15}{4} = 3\frac{3}{4}$

6. $\frac{2}{5} \div \frac{2}{7} = \frac{2}{5} \times \frac{7}{2} = \frac{14}{10} = \frac{7}{5} = 1\frac{2}{5}$

Page 58   Practice

1. $\frac{4}{5} \div 2 = \frac{4}{5} \div \frac{2}{1}$
$$= \frac{4}{5} \times \frac{1}{2}$$
$$= \frac{\overset{2}{\cancel{4}} \times 1}{5 \times \underset{1}{\cancel{2}}} = \frac{2}{5}$$

2. $3\frac{3}{4} \div \frac{1}{2} = \frac{15}{4} \div \frac{1}{2}$
$$= \frac{15}{4} \times \frac{2}{1}$$
$$= \frac{15 \times \overset{1}{\cancel{2}}}{\underset{2}{\cancel{4}} \times 1} = \frac{15}{2} = 7\frac{1}{2}$$

3. $6 \div 3\frac{1}{3} = \frac{6}{1} \div \frac{10}{3}$
$$= \frac{6}{1} \times \frac{3}{10}$$
$$= \frac{\overset{3}{\cancel{6}} \times 3}{1 \times \underset{5}{\cancel{10}}} = \frac{9}{5} = 1\frac{4}{5}$$

4. $2\frac{1}{4} \div 1\frac{1}{3} = \frac{9}{4} \div \frac{4}{3}$

$\qquad = \frac{9}{4} \times \frac{3}{4}$

$\qquad = \frac{9 \times 3}{4 \times 4} = \frac{27}{16} = 1\frac{11}{16}$

5. $2\frac{1}{8} \div 2\frac{1}{8} = \frac{17}{8} \div \frac{17}{8}$

$\qquad = \frac{17}{8} \times \frac{8}{17}$

$\qquad = \frac{\overset{1}{\cancel{17}} \times \overset{1}{\cancel{8}}}{\underset{1}{\cancel{8}} \times \underset{1}{\cancel{17}}} = 1$

6. $1\frac{2}{5} \div 3\frac{1}{4} = \frac{7}{5} \div \frac{13}{4}$

$\qquad = \frac{7}{5} \times \frac{4}{13}$

$\qquad = \frac{7 \times 4}{5 \times 13} = \frac{28}{65}$

Page 59 Self-Test

1. (5) 7 strips

$1\frac{3}{4} \div \frac{1}{4} = \frac{7}{4} \div \frac{1}{4}$

$\qquad = \frac{7}{4} \times \frac{4}{1}$

$\qquad = \frac{7 \times \overset{1}{\cancel{4}}}{\underset{1}{\cancel{4}} \times 1} = 7$

2. (2) $2\frac{1}{2}$ recipes

$3\frac{1}{3} \div 1\frac{1}{3} = \frac{10}{3} \div \frac{4}{3}$

$\qquad = \frac{10}{3} \times \frac{3}{4}$

$\qquad = \frac{\overset{5}{\cancel{10}} \times \overset{1}{\cancel{3}}}{\underset{1}{\cancel{3}} \times \underset{2}{\cancel{4}}} = \frac{5}{2} = 2\frac{1}{2}$

3. (2) 10 bags

$25 \div 2\frac{1}{2} = \frac{25}{1} \div \frac{5}{2}$

$\qquad = \frac{25}{1} \times \frac{2}{5}$

$\qquad = \frac{\overset{5}{\cancel{25}} \times 2}{1 \times \underset{1}{\cancel{5}}} = 10$

4. (4) $7\frac{1}{2}$ alterations

$3\frac{3}{4} \div \frac{1}{2} = \frac{15}{4} \div \frac{1}{2}$

$\qquad = \frac{15}{4} \times \frac{2}{1}$

$\qquad = \frac{15 \times \overset{1}{\cancel{2}}}{\underset{2}{\cancel{4}} \times 1} = \frac{15}{2} = 7\frac{1}{2}$

5. (2) 6 trips

$8 \div 1\frac{1}{3} = \frac{8}{1} \div \frac{4}{3}$

$\qquad = \frac{8}{1} \times \frac{3}{4}$

$\qquad = \frac{\overset{2}{\cancel{8}} \times 3}{1 \times \underset{1}{\cancel{4}}} = 6$

Page 60 Self-Test

6. (1) $\frac{2}{3}$ lb

$3\frac{1}{3} \div 5 = \frac{10}{3} \div \frac{5}{1}$

$\qquad = \frac{10}{3} \times \frac{1}{5}$

$\qquad = \frac{\overset{2}{\cancel{10}} \times 1}{3 \times \underset{1}{\cancel{5}}} = \frac{2}{3}$

7. (4) 6 pieces

$4\frac{1}{2} \div \frac{3}{4} = \frac{9}{2} \div \frac{3}{4}$

$\qquad = \frac{9}{2} \times \frac{4}{3}$

$\qquad = \frac{\overset{3}{\cancel{9}} \times \overset{2}{\cancel{4}}}{\underset{1}{\cancel{2}} \times \underset{1}{\cancel{3}}} = 6$

8. (3) $3\frac{1}{2}$ posts

$4\frac{2}{3} \div 1\frac{1}{3} = \frac{14}{3} \div \frac{4}{3}$

$\qquad = \frac{14}{3} \times \frac{3}{4}$

$\qquad = \frac{\overset{7}{\cancel{14}} \times \overset{1}{\cancel{3}}}{\underset{1}{\cancel{3}} \times \underset{2}{\cancel{4}}} = \frac{7}{2} = 3\frac{1}{2}$

9. (5) 6 trips

$\frac{3}{4} \div \frac{1}{8} = \frac{3}{4} \times \frac{8}{1}$

$\qquad = \frac{3 \times \overset{2}{\cancel{8}}}{\underset{1}{\cancel{4}} \times 1} = 6$

10. (1) $\frac{5}{12}$ acre

$8\frac{1}{3} \div 20 = \frac{25}{3} \div \frac{20}{1}$

$\qquad = \frac{25}{3} \times \frac{1}{20}$

$\qquad = \frac{\overset{5}{\cancel{25}} \times 1}{3 \times \underset{4}{\cancel{20}}} = \frac{5}{12}$

DECIMALS

YOU already know something about decimals because our money system — dollars and cents — is based on decimals. In this unit, you will learn more about decimals and you will learn new skills. You will continue to practice the skills you used in earlier units too. The most important of these skills is deciding how to solve a problem. Knowing when to add, subtract, multiply, or divide is a skill that is useful no matter what kind of numbers you work with.

1. DECIMALS

A part of a whole is called a fraction. We sometimes talk about money in terms of fractions:

$$\text{a half dollar} = \tfrac{1}{2} \text{ dollar} = 50 \text{ cents}$$
$$\text{a quarter} = \tfrac{1}{4} \text{ dollar} = 25 \text{ cents}$$

The word "cents" comes from the Latin word *centum*. *Centum* means "one hundred."

A dollar is divided into 100 equal parts. Each part is called a cent or a penny. A single cent or penny can be written as $\tfrac{1}{100}$, or *one hundredth* of a dollar. 95 cents can be written this way:

$$95 \text{ cents} = \tfrac{95}{100} \text{ dollar}$$

Amounts of money greater than a dollar can be written using the same method.

$$12 \text{ dollars and } 95 \text{ cents} = \$12\tfrac{95}{100}$$

Some people write bank checks this way. An easier way of writing this amount is:

$$12 \text{ dollars and } 95 \text{ cents} = \$12.95$$

This way of writing a fraction is called a *decimal*. The decimal point separates the whole number from the fraction. The whole number is to the left of the decimal point and the fraction is to the right.

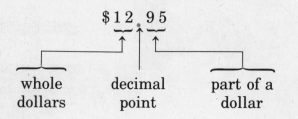

whole dollars   decimal point   part of a dollar

Dollars and cents are written using a decimal point.   Any fraction with 100 in the denominator can be written as a decimal too.

$\frac{36}{100}$ = 0.36   thirty-six hundredths

$3\frac{48}{100}$ = 3.48   three and forty-eight hundredths

$106\frac{92}{100}$ = 106.92 one hundred six and ninety-two hundredths

Notice that "and" is used for the decimal point.   106 should be read as "one hundred six" and *not* as "one hundred and six."

For hundredths, there are always two places after the decimal point.   What if you have an amount of money such as 4 dollars and 2 cents ($\frac{2}{100}$)?   This is written as:

$4.02

Notice the zero that has been put in to fill out two places after the decimal point.

Other fractions can also be written as decimals.   A fraction with 10 in the denominator can be written this way:

$\frac{3}{10}$ or 0.3   three-tenths

A gas pump measures the gas you put in your car in *tenths* of a gallon.   "11.3" on the pump means "eleven and three-tenths" gallons.

Practice.   Write each fraction as a decimal.   Then compare your answers with those in *Answers and Solutions* on page 86.

1. $\frac{9}{10}$ 2. $\frac{8}{100}$ 3. $18\frac{1}{10}$ 4. $14\frac{32}{100}$ 5. $4\frac{2}{10}$ 6. $3\frac{43}{100}$

2. ADDING AND SUBTRACTING DECIMALS

It is usually easier to work with decimals than with fractions.   Look at how you add a half dollar and a quarter.

with fractions:

Step 1. $\frac{1}{2}$ dollar $= \frac{2}{4}$ dollar

Step 2. $\frac{2}{4}$ dollar

$+ \frac{1}{4}$ dollar

$\overline{\frac{3}{4} \text{ dollar}}$

with decimals:

$$
\begin{array}{r}
\$\ .5\,0 \\
+\ \$\ .2\,5 \\
\hline
\$\ .7\,5
\end{array}
$$

Example:

What is the total of $86.12 and $19.42?

The only new rule in adding or subtracting decimals is:
Keep the decimal points lined up, one under the other.

$$
\begin{array}{r}
\$\ \ \ 8\,6.1\,2 \\
+\ \$\ \ \ 1\,9.4\,2 \\
\hline
\$\ 1\,0\,5.5\,4
\end{array}
$$

Example:

Rita had $10 in her pocketbook.   She bought a book for $7.95.   How much money did she have left?

If a whole number is written without a decimal point, place a decimal point and zeros at the end of the number.

$$\$10 = \$10.00$$

$$
\begin{array}{r}
\$\ 1\,0.0\,0 \\
-\ \$\ \ \ 7.9\,5 \\
\end{array}
$$

$$
\begin{array}{r}
{}^{9} \\
{}^{9}\ {}^{10}{}^{10} \\
\$\ 1\,0.0\,0 \\
-\ \$\ \ \ 7.9\,5 \\
\hline
\$\ \ \ 2.0\,5
\end{array}
$$

Notice that you can borrow right across the decimal point.

Example:

Peter has two containers of chemicals in his shop. The first container weighs 37.1 ounces. The second container weighs 9.82 ounces. What is the difference in weights?

Line up the decimal points.

$$\begin{array}{r} 3\ 7.1 \\ -\ \ \ 9.8\ 2 \\ \hline \end{array}$$

Place a zero so both numbers are in hundredths.

$$\begin{array}{r} 3\ 7.1\ 0 \\ -\ \ \ 9.8\ 2 \\ \hline \end{array}$$

Subtract, borrowing when necessary.

$$\begin{array}{r} 3\ 7.1\ 0 \\ -\ \ \ 9.8\ 2 \\ \hline 2\ 7.2\ 8 \end{array}$$

The first container weighs 27.28 ounces more than the second container.

Practice. Add or subtract. Then compare your answers with those in *Answers and Solutions* on page 86.

1. 78.02 + 46.39

2. 58.38 − 21.41

3. 56.81 + 4.3

4. 51.37 − 48.6

5. 7 − 1.53

6. 4.31 + 82.5 + 20

Self-Test

Solve these problems. Put an X next to the correct answer. Then compare your answers with those in *Answers and Solutions* on page 86.

Addition and subtraction word problems with decimals.

1. On Monday, Langston put 12.4 gallons of gas in his car. On the following Saturday, he put in 9.7 gallons. How much gas did Langston put in his car that week?

____ (1) 2.7 gallons
____ (2) 18.1 gallons
____ (3) 21.1 gallons
____ (4) 22.1 gallons
____ (5) 31.1 gallons

2. The area of the United States is 3.6 million sq mi. The area of Canada is 3.9 million sq miles. How much larger is Canada than the United States?

____ (1) 0.3 million sq mi
____ (2) 3 million sq mi
____ (3) 3.3 million sq mi
____ (4) 7.5 million sq mi
____ (5) 75 million sq mi

3. Mr. Neil wrote two checks last evening: one check to the phone company for $28.79 and the other to the gas and electric company for $45.17. What was the total of the two checks?

____ (1) $16.38
____ (2) $23.62
____ (3) $37.96
____ (4) $63.96
____ (5) $73.96

4. When the Cruz family started on a trip, they had 8,326.4 miles on their car. At the end of the trip, they had 8,921.2 miles. How far did they go on their trip?

____ (1) 504.8 miles
____ (2) 584.8 miles
____ (3) 594.8 miles
____ (4) 604.8 miles
____ (5) 605.8 miles

5. Mrs. Juarez's daughter was sick with the flu. Her temperature rose to 103.2 degrees. Her normal temperature is 98.6 degrees. How much higher than normal was her temperature?

____ (1) 0.46 degrees
____ (2) 0.54 degrees
____ (3) 4.6 degrees
____ (4) 5.4 degrees
____ (5) 46 degrees

6. Mr. Park mailed 3 packages weighing 12 pounds, 5.4 pounds, and 1.9 pounds. What was the total weight of the packages he mailed?

____ (1) 8.5 lb

____ (2) 9.3 lb

____ (3) 18.3 lb

____ (4) 19.3 lb

____ (5) 29.3 lb

7. On his first lift, a weight lifter lifted 196.5 lb. On his second lift, he lifted 217 lb. How much more did he lift the second time?

____ (1) 17.5 lb

____ (2) 20.5 lb

____ (3) 21.5 lb

____ (4) 22.5 lb

____ (5) 121.5 lb

8. At the beginning of the week, a jeweler had 52.13 ounces of gold on hand. At the end of the week, he had 29.04 ounces. How much gold did the jeweler use during the week?

____ (1) 23.09 ounces

____ (2) 23.17 ounces

____ (3) 23.19 ounces

____ (4) 33.19 ounces

____ (5) 33.04 ounces

9. Khamla had a quiz average of 76.8. By the end of the term she had raised her average by 3.4 points. What was her quiz average at the end of the term?

____ (1) 70.2

____ (2) 73.4

____ (3) 79.2

____ (4) 79.4

____ (5) 80.2

10. Ralph Hom has a delivery job. One week he drove the following distances: Monday, 87.5 miles; Tuesday, 39.1 miles; Wednesday, 105 miles; Thursday, 63.2 miles; Friday, 50.9 miles. What was his total mileage for the week?

____ (1) 251.2 miles

____ (2) 306.6 miles

____ (3) 345.7 miles

____ (4) 405.7 miles

____ (5) 445.7 miles

3. MULTIPLYING DECIMALS

Multiplying decimals is almost the same as multiplying whole numbers.

Example:

Hamburger costs $1.48 a pound this week. How much will 5 pounds cost?

In multiplying decimals, you do not need to line up the decimal points. First you multiply.

$$\begin{array}{r} \$\,1.4\,8 \\ \times\qquad 5 \\ \hline \$\,7\,4\,0 \end{array}$$

Then you place the decimal point. There are two numbers to the right of the decimal point in the problem. So the answer will also have two places to the right of the decimal point.

$$\begin{array}{r} \$\,1.4\,8 \\ \times\qquad 5 \\ \hline \$\,7.4\,0 \end{array}$$ two places

two places

Be sure to look at the answer to see if it makes sense. For example, in the problem above, $74 would be too high for 5 pounds of hamburger and $0.74 would be too low. $7.40 is the right answer.

When multiplying with decimals, it doesn't matter which number is on top.

Example:

A store ordered a shipment of 18 gift boxes of cheeses and smoked meats. Each box weighs 10.7 lb. How much will the shipment weigh?

$$\begin{array}{r} 1\,8 \\ \times\ 1\,0.7 \\ \hline 1\,2\,6 \\ 0\,0\,0 \\ 1\,8\quad \\ \hline 1\,9\,2.6 \end{array}$$ one place

one place

$$\begin{array}{r} 1\,0.7 \\ \times\qquad 1\,8 \\ \hline 8\,5\,6 \\ 1\,0\,7\quad \\ \hline 1\,9\,2.6 \end{array}$$ one place

one place

When multiplying, if both numbers are decimals, you count the numbers to the right of the decimal point in *both* numbers.

Example:

Roberta bought 12.8 gallons of gas at $1.26 per gallon. How much did she pay?

$$
\begin{array}{r}
\$ 1.2\,6 \quad \text{\_two places} \qquad 2 \\
\times \quad 1\,2.8 \quad \text{one place} \qquad +\,1 \\
\hline
1\,0\,0\,8 \qquad\qquad 3 \\
2\,5\,2 \\
1\,2\,6 \\
\hline
\$\,1\,6.1\,2\,8
\end{array}
$$

The answer will have 3 places. Count 3 places in *from the right.*

Roberta paid $16.13.

FOR YOUR INFORMATION

Because there is no way to pay exactly $16.128 for a tank of gas, the amount should be rounded. To round to the nearest cent, look at the number to the right of the cents place (8). If it is 4 or less, leave the cents unchanged. If it is 5 or greater, round up. Because 8 is greater than 5, $16.128 rounds to $16.13.

Practice. Multiply. Then compare your answers with those in *Answers and Solutions* on page 86.

1. 92.03 × 41

2. 7.6 × 5.51

3. $5.08 × 25

4. 66.8 × 7.2

5. 841 × 2.1

6. $3.08 × 6.4

Multiply and round to the nearest cent.

7. $1.14 × 1.2

8. $10.79 × 0.3

9. $1.215 × 14

Self-Test

Solve these problems. Put an X next to the correct answer. Then compare your answers with those in *Answers and Solutions* on page 86.

Multiplication problems with decimals.

1. Straw hats are on sale at $5.25 each. If Mrs. Loomis buys one for each of her eight grandchildren, how much will the hats cost altogether?

    _____ (1) $4.20

    _____ (2) $13.25

    _____ (3) $38.25

    _____ (4) $42.00

    _____ (5) $45.20

2. A family used 540 kilowatt-hours of electricity in one month. If the charge is $0.08 per kilowatt-hour, how much was their bill for the month?

    _____ (1) $4.32

    _____ (2) $25.06

    _____ (3) $26.50

    _____ (4) $43.20

    _____ (5) $48.30

3. Ming drives 10.4 miles to work every day. How far does he drive both ways?

    _____ (1) 10.8 miles

    _____ (2) 18.8 miles

    _____ (3) 20.8 miles

    _____ (4) 28 miles

    _____ (5) 28.4 miles

4. A man had a dinner at a restaurant. His bill was $8.50. He wanted to leave a tip equal to $\frac{1}{10}$, or 0.1, of his bill. How much was the tip?

    _____ (1) $0.75

    _____ (2) $0.85

    _____ (3) $1.00

    _____ (4) $1.05

    _____ (5) $1.85

5. Anita bought 10.7 gallons of gasoline for her car. The gasoline cost $1.33 a gallon. How much did she pay for the gas?

    _____ (1) $2.26

    _____ (2) $14.23

    _____ (3) $14.24

    _____ (4) $22.60

    _____ (5) $142.31

6. In a certain chemical mixture, $\frac{9}{10}$ (0.9) of the solution must be salt. If the mixture is 86.39 ounces, how much is salt?

____ (1) 77.751 oz

____ (2) 79.705 oz

____ (3) 86.359 oz

____ (4) 96.35 oz

____ (5) 96.359 oz

7. Helen's Beauty Shop serves its customers free coffee. The coffee pot makes 9.5 cups of coffee at a time. One busy day, Helen made coffee 6 times. How much coffee was served?

____ (1) 5.4 cups

____ (2) 5.7 cups

____ (3) 54 cups

____ (4) 57 cups

____ (5) 570 cups

8. The average price spent for lunch at a cafeteria is $3.62. If 35 people come through the line in an hour, how much money does the cashier take in?

____ (1) $105

____ (2) $106.60

____ (3) $107.60

____ (4) $116.60

____ (5) $126.70

9. A light wool fabric is $6.75 per yard. What is the cost of 3.4 yards of the fabric?

____ (1) $20.63

____ (2) $22.85

____ (3) $22.95

____ (4) $27

____ (5) $229.50

10. Doyle Culter stocks the dairy section of a grocery store. Sometimes he must lift a crate containing 6 gallons of milk. A gallon of milk weighs 8.7 lb. How much does the crate weigh?

____ (1) 14.7 lb

____ (2) 52.2 lb

____ (3) 53.2 lb

____ (4) 482 lb

____ (5) 522 lb

4. DIVIDING WITH DECIMALS

Dividing a decimal by a whole number is similar to dividing with two whole numbers.

Example:

Jose bought 3 batteries for $4.71.   What is the price per battery?

By looking at the problem, you can see the answer will be somewhat more than $1. To find out the exact price, divide.

Notice that the answer has the same number of decimal places as the original price.

```
   1.5 7
3)4.7 1
  3
  1 7
  1 5
    2 1
    2 1
```

The price per battery is $1.57.

In longer division problems, it is sometimes necessary to put a zero at the end of a decimal in order to finish the division. Remember that putting a zero at the end of a decimal doesn't change its value.   For example,

```
    9.5              9.5
5)4 7.8          5)4 7.8 0
  4 5              4 5
    2 8              2 8
    2 5              2 5
      3                3 0
                       3 0
```

There are some division problems that won't come out evenly, no matter how many zeros you put on. For example,

$$
\begin{array}{r}
.3 \\
3\overline{)1.0} \\
\underline{9} \\
1
\end{array}
\qquad
\begin{array}{r}
.3\,3 \\
3\overline{)1.0\,0} \\
\underline{9} \\
1\,0 \\
\underline{9} \\
1
\end{array}
\qquad
\begin{array}{r}
.3\,3\,3 \\
3\overline{)1.0\,0\,0} \\
\underline{9} \\
1\,0 \\
\underline{9} \\
1\,0 \\
\underline{9} \\
1
\end{array}
$$

Here you can just round your answer. For example you can round to either 0.33 or 0.3.

Practice. Divide. Then compare your answers with those in *Answers and Solutions* on page 87.

1. 61 ÷ 10

2. 15.4 ÷ 5

3. 588 ÷ 5

4. 42 ÷ 12

5. 5.7 ÷ 6

6. 5.86 ÷ 20

To divide a decimal by another decimal, you must change the number you divide by to a whole number.

Example:

At a rummage sale, shirts cost $1.50 each.   How many shirts can you buy for $4.50?

One way to solve this is to count up the cost for shirts until you reach $4.50.

One shirt $1.50
Two shirts $3.00
Three shirts $4.50

The answer is 3 shirts.   This problem can also be solved by division.

$$1.5\,0\,)\overline{4.5\,0}$$

This problem is different from the decimal division problems you have seen so far because the outside number (the number you are dividing by) is a decimal.   To do the division, the outside number must be a whole number.   Here are steps for dividing decimals by decimals:

1. Move the decimal point until the outside number is a whole number.

$$1.5\,\underline{0}.\,)\overline{4.5\,0}$$

2. Move the decimal point of the inside number the same number of places.

$$1.5\,\underline{0}.\,)\overline{4.5\,\underline{0}.}$$

3. Divide.

$$\begin{array}{r} 3. \\ 1.5\,\underline{0}.\,)\overline{4.5\,\underline{0}.} \\ 4\,5\,0 \end{array}$$

Check your answer.
Multiply your answer by the number you divided by (the outside number).
You should get the inside number.

$$\begin{array}{r} \$\,1.5\,0 \\ \times\quad 3 \\ \hline \$\,4.5\,0 \end{array}$$

Example: Divide 0.72 by 0.3.

1. Move the decimal point of the outside number one place.

$$0.3_{.}\overline{)0.7\,2}$$

2. Move the decimal point of the inside number one place.
(Notice that the inside number does not become a whole number when its decimal point is moved.)

$$0.3_{.}\overline{)0.7_{.}2}$$

3. Divide.

$$\begin{array}{r} 2_{.}4 \\ 0.3_{.}\overline{)0.7_{.}2} \\ \underline{6} \\ 1\,2 \\ \underline{1\,2} \end{array}$$

Example: Divide 48 by 0.6.

1. Move the decimal point of the outside number one place.

$$0.6_{.}\overline{)4\,8}$$

2. Move the decimal point of the inside number one place.
(Notice that you must add a decimal point and a zero to the end of the inside number.)

$$0.6_{.}\overline{)4\,8.0_{.}}$$

3. Divide.

$$\begin{array}{r} 8\,0_{.} \\ 0.6_{.}\overline{)4\,8.0_{.}} \\ \underline{4\,8} \\ 0\,0 \\ \underline{0\,0} \end{array}$$

Practice. Divide. Then compare your answers with those in *Answers and Solutions* on page 87.

1. $1.5\overline{)7.5}$

2. $0.4\overline{)0.1\,2}$

3. $0.0\,7\overline{)0.1\,4}$

4. $5.2\overline{)1\,5\,6}$

5. $0.6\,1\overline{)2\,4.4}$

6. $2.3\overline{)0.1\,6\,1}$

STRATEGIES FOR SUCCESS

MAKING PROBLEMS EASIER TO WORK WITH

Sometimes there is extra information in a problem. Don't let this information confuse you. Also, estimating can help you decide if your answer is correct.

STRATEGY 1: **Identify the important information.**

Read the problem carefully. Find the information or the numbers you should use to solve the problem.

Example: What information or numbers do you have to use to solve this problem?

Mary and Alice went shopping together. Mary spent $5.98 on cosmetics. Alice bought a blouse for $13.95 and a skirt for $21.50. How much more did Alice spend for the skirt than the blouse?

This problem contains information about Mary and about Alice. The question asks only about Alice. The numbers that are necessary to solve this problem are $13.95 and $21.50. You can ignore the amount that Mary spent. *How much more* are key words for subtraction.

$$\begin{array}{r} \$21.50 \\ -13.95 \\ \hline \$7.55 \end{array}$$

Alice spent $7.55 more for the skirt.

Solve this problem. Use Strategy 1.

Ms. Mendez worked 35 hours this week at $6.50 an hour. She worked 8 hours of overtime at $9.75 too. How much did she earn this week in overtime?

- Underline the important information.
- What is the operation? _____
- What is the answer? _____

STRATEGY 2: Estimate your answer.

Estimating will help you recognize a correct answer.

Example: Estimate the answer and solve this problem.

Mr. Forest worked for a company for 25 years. When he retired his 12 co-workers bought him a watch which cost $103.40. How much did each person pay toward the gift?

First identify the important information: the cost of the watch ($103.40) and the number of people (12). Then round to numbers that are easy to work with. $103.40 rounds to $100 and 12 rounds to 10.

$$\$103.40 \rightarrow \$100$$
$$12 \rightarrow 10$$

Divide 100 by 10 to find the estimate.

$$10\overline{)\$100} = \$10$$

Then find the exact answer and compare to see if they are close. $8.62 is close to $10.00.

$$
\begin{array}{r}
\$\ \ \ 8.6\,1\,6 \\
1\,2\overline{)\$1\,0\,3.4\,0\,0} \\
9\,6 \\
\hline
7\,4 \\
7\,2 \\
\hline
2\,0 \\
1\,2 \\
\hline
8\,0 \\
7\,2 \\
\hline
8
\end{array}
$$

Each person paid $8.62.

Solve this problem.   First estimate the answer.   Use Strategy 2.

Bill Judson drives a delivery truck.   The truck he uses averages 18 miles per gallon of gasoline.   He drives an average of 150 miles a day.   How far can he go on 7.5 gallons of gasoline?

- What numbers are important? _____
- Round the numbers. _____
- What is your estimate? _____
- What is the exact answer? _____

Check your answers.   Ask yourself if the answers make sense.   Estimating is a good way to check your answers.

Compare your answers with those in *Answers and Solutions* on page 87.

$\mathcal{S}$elf-Test

Division problems with decimals.

1. Jean drove 281.6 miles on 11 gallons of gas. How many miles per gallon does her car get?

_____ (1) 2.56 mpg

_____ (2) 11 mpg

_____ (3) 25.6 mpg

_____ (4) 28.16 mpg

_____ (5) 31.2 mpg

2. George bought a five-pound family pack of chicken. He paid $3.95 for the package. How much did he pay per pound?

_____ (1) $0.39

_____ (2) $0.79

_____ (3) $1.28

_____ (4) $3.95

_____ (5) $5.00

3. If 12 gallons of gas cost $15.48, how much does 1 gallon cost?

_____ (1) $1.17

_____ (2) $1.20

_____ (3) $1.29

_____ (4) $1.54

_____ (5) $1.63

4. Marty is buying a jacket on the installment plan. The jacket costs $74.75. He pays $5.75 each week. How many weeks will it take him to pay for the jacket?

_____ (1) 13 weeks

_____ (2) 15 weeks

_____ (3) 19 weeks

_____ (4) 21 weeks

_____ (5) 23 weeks

5. When tomatoes were in season, Mrs. Rogers made a big batch of spaghetti sauce. She paid $4.64 for the tomatoes to use in the sauce. If the cost of the tomatoes was $0.29 a pound, how many pounds of tomatoes did she buy?

_____ (1) 1.6 lb

_____ (2) 2.6 lb

_____ (3) 10 lb

_____ (4) 12.6 lb

_____ (5) 16 lb

6. Ellie wants to freeze 8 pounds of hamburger in 5 equal packages. How much hamburger should she put in each package?

- _____ (1) 1.5 lb
- _____ (2) 1.6 lb
- _____ (3) 2 lb
- _____ (4) 5 lb
- _____ (5) 15 lb

7. A baseball player got 68 hits in 250 times at bat.   What was his batting average? (To find the average, divide the number of hits by the number of times at bat.)

- _____ (1) .250
- _____ (2) .262
- _____ (3) .272
- _____ (4) .305
- _____ (5) .312

8. A shipment of six lawn mowers weighs 1.5 tons.   How much does each mower weigh?

- _____ (1) 0.15 tons
- _____ (2) 0.25 tons
- _____ (3) 0.35 tons
- _____ (4) 0.6 tons
- _____ (5) 2.5 tons

9. 7 trout weigh a total of 5.95 pounds. What is the average weight of each fish?

- _____ (1) 0.55 lb
- _____ (2) 0.65 lb
- _____ (3) 0.75 lb
- _____ (4) 0.85 lb
- _____ (5) 0.9 lb

10. Last weekend Helene drove 157.6 miles to visit her mother.   It took her 3.2 hours to make the drive.   What was her average rate of speed?

- _____ (1) 29.25 miles per hour
- _____ (2) 33.5 miles per hour
- _____ (3) 45 miles per hour
- _____ (4) 49.2 miles per hour
- _____ (5) 49.25 miles per hour

Decide whether to add, subtract, multiply, or divide. Some of the problems require several steps.

11. Three friends were eating lunch at a restaurant. They decided to split the bill evenly. The total bill came to $16.02. How much did each one have to pay?

____ (1) $1.60
____ (2) $5.14
____ (3) $5.34
____ (4) $6.02
____ (5) $8.01

12. A jeweler was weighing gold. She had three pieces of gold. One weighed $1\frac{1}{4}$ oz, another weighed $2\frac{1}{3}$ oz, and the third weighed $1\frac{1}{2}$ oz. How much did she have altogether?

____ (1) 3.58 oz
____ (2) 3.83 oz
____ (3) 5 oz
____ (4) 5.08 oz
____ (5) 6.38 oz

13. A store is advertising sweaters on sale at $\frac{1}{4}$ off the regular price. If the regular price of a sweater is $26.00, how much can you save if you buy a sweater on sale?

____ (1) $6.50
____ (2) $7.00
____ (3) $7.50
____ (4) $13.00
____ (5) $25.00

14. The national debt was half a trillion dollars in 1975. By 1983, it had grown to 1.5 trillion dollars. How much had the national debt gone up during that time?

____ (1) 0.5 trillion dollars
____ (2) 0.7 trillion dollars
____ (3) 1 trillion dollars
____ (4) 1.5 trillion dollars
____ (5) 2 trillion dollars

15. Mrs. Rella is trying to decide whether to buy a new slipcover for the living room couch or to make one. She saw a slipcover in a department store for $39.95. To make a slipcover she would need 10 yards of fabric. The fabric costs $1.69 a yard and the thread costs $2.75. How much money would she save by making the slipcover?

____ (1) $12.45
____ (2) $16.90
____ (3) $19.65
____ (4) $20.30
____ (5) $23.05

16. The gas tank of Ray's car holds 22.4 gallons. How much gas is there in the tank when it is $\frac{3}{4}$ full?
___ (1) 3.4 gallons
___ (2) 4.6 gallons
___ (3) 8.6 gallons
___ (4) 12.8 gallons
___ (5) 16.8 gallons

17. If notebooks are 3 for $5.25, how much does each notebook cost?
___ (1) $1.42
___ (2) $1.75
___ (3) $1.85
___ (4) $1.87
___ (5) $1.95

18. A hunger relief committee collected $603.70 by the end of one week. By the end of one month, the amount had gone up $3\frac{1}{2}$ times. How much did the committee raise during that month?
___ (1) $1,923.74
___ (2) $1,931.84
___ (3) $2,112.95
___ (4) $2,225.84
___ (5) $2,795.94

19. Floyd had $325.47 in his checking account. He paid the telephone bill, which was $19.23. Then he paid the $37.42 electric bill. What was the balance left in Floyd's checking account?
___ (1) $268.82
___ (2) $279.82
___ (3) $289.82
___ (4) $307.28
___ (5) $343.66

20. Ralph Jackson does small catering jobs. He figures his prices by adding the cost of the ingredients plus the cost of his labor. The ingredients for a meal cost $30.95. It takes him $4\frac{1}{2}$ hours to prepare it and 1 hour to clean up afterwards. He figures his labor at $6.50 an hour. How much should he charge for the meal?
___ (1) $35.75
___ (2) $36.45
___ (3) $50.20
___ (4) $60.20
___ (5) $66.70

Answers and Solutions

Page 67   Practice
1. 0.9   **2.** 0.08   **3.** 18.1
4. 14.32   **5.** 4.2   **6.** 3.43

Page 69   Practice
1.
```
  7 8.0 2
+ 4 6.3 9
─────────
1 2 4.4 1
```
2.
```
  5 8.3 8
− 2 1.4 1
─────────
  3 6.9 7
```
3.
```
  5 6.8 1
+   4.3 0
─────────
  6 1.1 1
```

4.
```
  5 1.3 7
− 4 8.6 0
─────────
    2.7 7
```
5.
```
    7.0 0
−   1.5 3
─────────
    5.4 7
```
6.
```
    4.3 1
  8 2.5 0
+ 2 0.0 0
─────────
1 0 6.8 1
```

Page 70   Self-Test
1. (4) 22.1 gallons
```
  1 2.4
+   9.7
───────
  2 2.1
```

2. (1) 0.3 million sq miles
```
    3.9
−   3.6
───────
    0.3
```

3. (5) $73.96
```
$ 2 8.7 9
+   4 5.1 7
───────────
$ 7 3.9 6
```

4. (3) 594.8 miles
```
  8,9 2 1.2
− 8,3 2 6.4
───────────
    5 9 4.8
```

5. (3) 4.6 degrees
```
  1 0 3.2
−   9 8.6
─────────
      4.6
```

Page 71   Self-Test
6. (4) 19.3 lb   **7.** (2) 20.5 lb   **8.** (1) 23.09 oz
```
  1 2.0
    5.4
+   1.9
───────
  1 9.3
```
```
  2 1 7.0
− 1 9 6.5
─────────
    2 0.5
```
```
  5 2.1 3
− 2 9.0 4
─────────
  2 3.0 9
```

9. (5) 80.2   **10.** (3) 345.7 miles
```
  7 6.8
+   3.4
───────
  8 0.2
```
```
  8 7.5
  3 9.1
1 0 5.0
  6 3.2
+ 5 0.9
───────
3 4 5.7
```

Page 73   Practice
1.
```
  9 2.0 3
×     4 1
─────────
  9 2 0 3
3 6 8 1 2
─────────
3,7 7 3.2 3
```
2.
```
    7.6
×   5.5 1
─────────
    7 6
  3 8 0
3 8 0
─────────
4 1.8 7 6
```
3.
```
  $5.0 8
×     2 5
─────────
  2 5 4 0
1 0 1 6
─────────
$1 2 7.0 0
```

4.
```
    6 6.8
×    7.2
─────────
  1 3 3 6
4 6 7 6
─────────
4 8 0.9 6
```
5.
```
    8 4 1
×    2.1
─────────
    8 4 1
1 6 8 2
─────────
1,7 6 6.1
```

6.
```
  $3.0 8
×    6.4
─────────
  1 2 3 2
1 8 4 8
─────────
$1 9.7 1 2
```
7.
```
  $1.1 4
×    1.2
─────────
    2 2 8
1 1 4
─────────
$1.3 6 8 → $1.37
```

8.
```
$1 0.7 9
×    0.3
─────────
$3.2 3 7 → $3.24
```
9.
```
  $1.2 1 5
×      1 4
───────────
  4 8 6 0
1 2 1 5
───────────
$1 7.0 1 0 → $17.01
```

Page 74   Self-Test
1. (4) $42.00   **2.** (4) $43.20   **3.** (3) 20.8 miles
```
  $5.2 5
×      8
────────
$4 2.0 0
```
```
    5 4 0
×  $0.0 8
────────
$4 3.2 0
```
```
  1 0.4
×     2
───────
  2 0.8
```

4. (2) $0.85   **5.** (2) $14.23
```
  $8.5 0
×    0.1
────────
$.8 5 0 → $0.85
```
```
    $1.3 3
×    1 0.7
──────────
    9 3 1
  0 0 0
1 3 3
──────────
$1 4.2 3 1 → $14.23
```

Page 75   Self-Test
6. (1) 77.751 oz
```
  8 6.3 9
×    0.9
─────────
7 7.7 5 1
```

7. (4) 57 cups

$$\begin{array}{r} 9.5 \\ \times\ 6 \\ \hline 5\ 7.0 \end{array}$$

8. (5) $126.70

$$\begin{array}{r} \$3.6\ 2 \\ \times\ 3\ 5 \\ \hline 1\ 8\ 1\ 0 \\ 1\ 0\ 8\ 6 \\ \hline \$1\ 2\ 6.7\ 0 \end{array}$$

9. (3) $22.95

$$\begin{array}{r} \$6.7\ 5 \\ \times\ 3.4 \\ \hline 2\ 7\ 0\ 0 \\ 2\ 0\ 2\ 5 \\ \hline \$2\ 2.9\ 5\ 0 \to \$22.95 \end{array}$$

10. (2) 52.2 lb

$$\begin{array}{r} 8.7 \\ \times\ 6 \\ \hline 5\ 2.2 \end{array}$$

Page 77 Practice

1.
$$\begin{array}{r} 6.1 \\ 1\,0\,)\overline{6\ 1.0} \\ \underline{6\ 0} \\ 1\ 0 \\ \underline{1\ 0} \end{array}$$

2.
$$\begin{array}{r} 3.0\ 8 \\ 5\,)\overline{1\ 5.4\ 0} \\ \underline{1\ 5} \\ 4 \\ \underline{0} \\ 4\ 0 \\ \underline{4\ 0} \end{array}$$

3.
$$\begin{array}{r} 1\ 1\ 7.6 \\ 5\,)\overline{5\ 8\ 8.0} \\ \underline{5} \\ 8 \\ \underline{5} \\ 3\ 8 \\ \underline{3\ 5} \\ 3\ 0 \\ \underline{3\ 0} \end{array}$$

4.
$$\begin{array}{r} 3.5 \\ 1\,2\,)\overline{4\ 2.0} \\ \underline{3\ 6} \\ 6\ 0 \\ \underline{6\ 0} \end{array}$$

5.
$$\begin{array}{r} 0.9\ 5 \\ 6\,)\overline{5.7\ 0} \\ \underline{5\ 4} \\ 3\ 0 \\ \underline{3\ 0} \end{array}$$

6.
$$\begin{array}{r} 0.2\ 9\ 3 \\ 2\,0\,)\overline{5.8\ 6\ 0} \\ \underline{4\ 0} \\ 1\ 8\ 6 \\ \underline{1\ 8\ 0} \\ 6\ 0 \\ \underline{6\ 0} \end{array}$$

Page 79 Practice

1.
$$\begin{array}{r} 5. \\ 1.5\,)\overline{7.5} \\ \underline{7\ 5} \end{array}$$

2.
$$\begin{array}{r} 0.3 \\ 0.4\,)\overline{0.1\ 2} \\ \underline{0\ 1\ 2} \end{array}$$

3.
$$\begin{array}{r} 2. \\ 0.0\ 7\,)\overline{0.1\ 4} \\ \underline{0\ 1\ 4} \end{array}$$

4.
$$\begin{array}{r} 3\ 0. \\ 5.2\,)\overline{1\ 5\ 6.0} \\ \underline{1\ 5\ 6} \end{array}$$

5.
$$\begin{array}{r} 4\ 0. \\ 0.6\ 1\,)\overline{2\ 4.4\ 0} \\ \underline{2\ 4\ 4} \end{array}$$

6.
$$\begin{array}{r} .0\ 7 \\ 2.3\,)\overline{0.1\ 6\ 1} \\ \underline{0\ 1\ 6\ 1} \end{array}$$

Page 80 Strategies For Success

- 8 hours, $9.75
- multiplication
- $78.00

$$\begin{array}{r} \$9.7\ 5 \\ \times\ 8 \\ \hline \$7\ 8.0\ 0 \end{array}$$

Page 81 Strategies For Success

- 18, 7.5
- 20, 8
- 160 miles
- 135 miles

$18 \to 20$
$7.5 \to 8$

$$\begin{array}{r} 2\ 0 \\ \times\ 8 \\ \hline 1\ 6\ 0 \end{array}$$

$$\begin{array}{r} 1\ 8 \\ \times\ 7.5 \\ \hline 9\ 0 \\ 1\ 2\ 6 \\ \hline 1\ 3\ 5.0 \end{array}$$

Page 82 Self-Test

1. (3) 25.6 mpg

$$\begin{array}{r} 2\ 5.6 \\ 1\,1\,)\overline{2\ 8\ 1.6} \\ \underline{2\ 2} \\ 6\ 1 \\ \underline{5\ 5} \\ 6\ 6 \\ \underline{6\ 6} \end{array}$$

2. (2) $0.79

$$\begin{array}{r} \$\ .7\ 9 \\ 5\,)\overline{\$3.9\ 5} \\ \underline{3\ 5} \\ 4\ 5 \\ \underline{4\ 5} \end{array}$$

3. (3) $1.29

$$\begin{array}{r} \$\ 1.2\ 9 \\ 1\,2\,)\overline{\$1\ 5.4\ 8} \\ \underline{1\ 2} \\ 3\ 4 \\ \underline{2\ 4} \\ 1\ 0\ 8 \\ \underline{1\ 0\ 8} \end{array}$$

4. (1) 13 weeks

```
        1 3.
5.7 5.)7 4.7 5.
        5 7 5
        1 7 2 5
        1 7 2 5
```

5. (5) 16 lb

```
          1 6.
0.2 9.)4.6 4.
         2 9
         1 7 4
         1 7 4
```

Page 83   Self-Test

6. (2) 1.6 lb

```
      1.6
5 )8.0
      5
      3 0
      3 0
```

7. (3) .272

```
          .2 7 2
2 5 0 )6 8.0 0 0
          5 0 0
          1 8 0 0
          1 7 5 0
            5 0 0
            5 0 0
```

8. (2) 0.25 tons

```
      .2 5
6 )1.5 0
      1 2
      3 0
      3 0
```

9. (4) 0.85 lb

```
      .8 5
7 )5.9 5
      5 6
      3 5
      3 5
```

10. (5) 49.25 miles per hour

```
            4 9.2 5
3.2. )1 5 7.6.0 0
         1 2 8
           2 9 6
           2 8 8
             8 0
             6 4
             1 6 0
             1 6 0
```

Page 84   Self-Test

11. (3) $5.34

```
         $  5.3 4
3 )$1 6.0 2
      1 5
        1 0
          9
          1 2
          1 2
```

12. (4) 5.08 oz

$$1\frac{1}{4} = 1.2\,5$$
$$2\frac{1}{3} = 2.3\,3$$
$$+ 1\frac{1}{2} = 1.5\,0$$
$$\overline{\phantom{+ 1\frac{1}{2} = }\,5.0\,8}$$

13. (1) $6.50

$$\frac{1}{4} = 0.25$$

```
       $2 6
     × 0.2 5
       1 3 0
        5 2
     $6.5 0
```

14. (3) 1 trillion dollars

$$\frac{1}{2} = 0.5$$

```
       1.5
     − 0.5
       1.0
```

15. (4) $20.30

```
   $1.6 9        $1 6.9 0        $3 9.9 5
   ×  1 0        +   2.7 5       −  1 9.6 5
   0 0 0         $1 9.6 5        $2 0.3 0
   1 6 9
   $1 6.9 0
```

Page 85   Self-Test

16. (5) 16.8 gallons

$$\frac{3}{4} = 0.75$$

```
       2 2.4
     × 0.7 5
       1 1 2 0
       1 5 6 8
       1 6.8 0 0
```

17. (2) $1.75

```
         $1.7 5
3 )$5.2 5
      3
      2 2
      2 1
        1 5
        1 5
```

18. (3) 2,112.95

$$3\frac{1}{2} = 3.5$$

```
          $6 0 3.7 0
          ×     3.5
          3 0 1 8 5 0
          1 8 1 1 1 0
          $2,1 1 2.9 5 0
```

19. (1) $268.82

```
        $3 2 5.4 7
      −      1 9.2 3
        $3 0 6.2 4
      −      3 7.4 2
        $2 6 8.8 2
```

20. (5) $66.70

```
     4 1/2
   +   1
     5 1/2  = 5.5
```

```
   $6.5 0          $3 0.9 5
   ×  5.5          +  3 5.7 5
   3 2 5 0         $6 6.7 0
   3 2 5 0
   $3 5.7 5 0
```

P E R C E N T

PERCENT is used when businesses advertise sales. Percent is used to describe interest rates for savings accounts and loans. It is used to tell how much things increase or decrease in size, number or price. Increases and decreases in percent affect how much you spend and save.

In this unit, you will learn how to solve problems using percents. You will learn how to write a percent as a decimal or a fraction. And you will learn how to find the percent of a specific number.

1. PERCENT

Percent can be thought of as a particular type of fraction. Percent means hundredths. Percents are fractions with 100 in the denominator. The symbol for percent is written like this: "%."

$$1\% = 1 \text{ hundredth} = \frac{1}{100} \qquad 35\% = 35 \text{ hundredths} = \frac{35}{100}$$

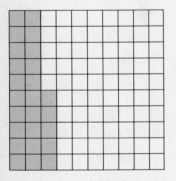

What percent of the large square is shaded?

25 out of 100 small squares are shaded.

$$\frac{25}{100} = 25\%$$

75 of the small squares are not shaded.

$$\frac{75}{100} = 75\%$$

The total number of small squares is 100.

$$\frac{100}{100} = 100\%$$

Notice that the percent of the large square that is shaded plus the percent of the large square that isn't shaded is 100%.

$$25\% + 75\% = 100\%$$

The whole square adds up to 100%. 100% means the whole of anything.

Knowing that the total is 100% can be used to solve problems.

Example:

14% of a company's employees are absent from work on Friday. What percent are at work on Friday?

$$\begin{array}{rl} 100\% & \text{total employees} \\ -\ \ 14\% & \text{percent absent} \\ \hline 86\% & \text{percent at work} \end{array}$$

*F*OR YOUR INFORMATION

It can be helpful to memorize some of the common fraction and percent equivalents. Here is a list that you can refer to:

$1\% = \frac{1}{100}$	$33\frac{1}{3}\% = \frac{1}{3}$	$75\% = \frac{3}{4}$
$5\% = \frac{1}{20}$	$40\% = \frac{2}{5}$	$80\% = \frac{4}{5}$
$10\% = \frac{1}{10}$	$50\% = \frac{1}{2}$	$90\% = \frac{9}{10}$
$20\% = \frac{1}{5}$	$60\% = \frac{3}{5}$	$99\% = \frac{99}{100}$
$25\% = \frac{1}{4}$	$66\frac{2}{3}\% = \frac{2}{3}$	$100\% = 1$
$30\% = \frac{3}{10}$	$70\% = \frac{7}{10}$	

Practice. Write the answers. Be sure to reduce fractions if possible. Then compare your answers with those in *Answers and Solutions* on page 103.

Write the fraction for each percent.

1. 10%   **2.** 35%   **3.** 3%   **4.** 75%

5. 62%   **6.** 50%   **7.** 95%   **8.** 45%

Write the percent for each fraction.

9. $\frac{37}{100}$ **10.** 2 hundredths   **11.** $\frac{2}{3}$ **12.** $\frac{13}{100}$

13. $\frac{2}{5}$ **14.** 49 hundredths   **15.** $\frac{3}{20}$ **16.** $\frac{1}{4}$

2. FINDING THE PERCENT OF A NUMBER

To change a percent to a decimal is very easy.   Since percents are hundredths, just change hundredths to a decimal.

$$15\% = \frac{15}{100} = 0.15$$

In other words, move the decimal point 2 places to the left and drop the % sign.   For example:

10% = 0.10	75% = 0.75	100% = 1.00
05% = 0.05	00.5% = 0.005	125% = 1.25

Notice that for 5% and 0.5% you had to write a zero to give the necessary 2 places.

Percents are changed to fractions or decimals because they are easier to work with in problems.

Example:

Angela wants to buy a dress which is on sale.   The dress regularly costs $86.   How much will she save if the dress is on sale for 25% off the regular price?

The question is, "What is 25% of $86?"   The word *of* shows that you have to multiply.   But how do you multiply 25% × $86?

Step 1.   Change the percent to a decimal.   25% = 0.25

Step 2.   Multiply.

$$\begin{array}{r} \$8\,6 \\ \times\ 0.2\,5 \\ \hline 4\,3\,0 \\ 1\,7\,2 \\ \hline \$2\,1.5\,0 \end{array}$$

She will save $21.50 by buying the dress on sale.

To find the percent of a number, change the percent to a decimal and multiply.

Example:

The sale price of Angela's dress is $64.50.   If the sales tax is 5%, how much tax will Angela have to pay?

Step 1. Change the percent   5% = 0.05
to a decimal.

Step 2. Multiply.

$$\begin{array}{r} \$6\ 4.5\ 0 \\ \times\ \ 0.0\ 5 \\ \hline \$3.2\ 2\ 5\ 0 \end{array}\ \text{or}\ \$3.23$$

The tax is $3.23.

To review rounding money, see page 73.

Percents aren't used only for money problems.

Example:

A restaurant ordered 70 pounds of pastry flour. 15% of the order did not come in.   How many pounds of flour were missing?

Step 1.   15% = 0.15

Step 2.

$$\begin{array}{r} 0.1\ 5 \\ \times\ \ 7\ 0 \\ \hline 1\ 0.5\ 0 \end{array}\ \text{or}\ 10.5\ \text{lb}$$

Practice.   Answer these questions.   Then compare your answers with those in *Answers and Solutions* on page 103.

1. What is 10% of 54?   **2.** What is 75% of 48?   **3.** What is 40% of 26.5?

4. What is 100% of 37?   **5.** What is 5% of 150?   **6.** What is 1% of 92?

Self-Test

Word problems with percent.

1. A man worked for 20 hours to redecorate his kitchen. He figured that he had spent 50% of that time painting. How much time was spent painting?

____ (1) 2 hours

____ (2) 10 hours

____ (3) 20 hours

____ (4) 40 hours

____ (5) 50 hours

2. Cynthia cut a pie into 8 pieces for her family. The family ate all 8 pieces. How much of the pie was eaten?

____ (1) 8%

____ (2) 20%

____ (3) 50%

____ (4) 80%

____ (5) 100%

3. Erica has decided to spend 60% of her savings on a trip. She has $987.60 in the bank. How much is she going to spend on the trip?

____ (1) $395.04

____ (2) $541.56

____ (3) $545.60

____ (4) $592.56

____ (5) $692.50

4. Len Richardson got a 10% raise in pay. What fraction is this?

____ (1) $\frac{1}{100}$

____ (2) $\frac{1}{10}$

____ (3) $\frac{1}{4}$

____ (4) $\frac{1}{3}$

____ (5) $\frac{1}{2}$

5. Alicia Tom paid 30% of her salary last year in taxes. What percent of her salary did she have left after taxes?

____ (1) 3%

____ (2) 15%

____ (3) 50%

____ (4) 70%

____ (5) 85%

6. The Chang family has just had dinner in a restaurant. They want to leave a 15% tip on a bill of $24.80. How much tip should they leave?

_____ (1) $3.62

_____ (2) $3.72

_____ (3) $3.92

_____ (4) $4.22

_____ (5) $4.40

7. 36% of the people attending a night school drive to school. If 225 people go to the school, how many drive?

_____ (1) 81 people

_____ (2) 90 people

_____ (3) 93 people

_____ (4) 101 people

_____ (5) 144 people

8. On an automobile trip, Susan drove 55% of the time. Her husband drove the rest. If the trip was 382 miles long, how many miles did Susan drive?

_____ (1) 185.1 miles

_____ (2) 191 miles

_____ (3) 198.1 miles

_____ (4) 201.1 miles

_____ (5) 210.1 miles

9. 62% of a shipment was apples. The shipment weighed 500 pounds. How many pounds of apples were in the shipment?

_____ (1) 190 lb

_____ (2) 210 lb

_____ (3) 290 lb

_____ (4) 310 lb

_____ (5) 320 lb

10. Lionel Washington has a roadside fruit stand. He bought $400 worth of fruit. 15% of the fruit spoiled before he could sell it. How much money did he lose?

_____ (1) $6.00

_____ (2) $50.25

_____ (3) $60.00

_____ (4) $75.25

_____ (5) $100.00

3. PERCENT PROBLEMS WITH SEVERAL STEPS

Percent problems often take several steps to solve.

Example:

> 250 tickets were sold for a school band concert.   But
> due to bad weather, 12% of the ticket holders did not
> come.   How many people came to the concert?

Find 12% of 250.

Step 1.   Change the percent   12% = 0.12
to a decimal.

Step 2.   Multiply.

$$
\begin{array}{r}
2\,5\,0 \\
\times\ 0.1\,2 \\
\hline
5\,0\,0 \\
2\,5\,0\ \ \\
\hline
3\,0.0\,0
\end{array}
$$

Will you add or subtract?   Picture the situation.   250 tickets were
sold, but there was bad weather that kept some away.   Fewer
people showed up, so subtract.

Step 3.   Subtract.

$$
\begin{array}{r}
2\,5\,0 \\
-\ \ 3\,0 \\
\hline
2\,2\,0
\end{array}
$$

220 people came to the concert.

Sometimes there are not many words in a problem.   But
it may take several steps to find the answer.

Example:

> A pair of shoes usually costs $46.   How much will they cost
> if they are on sale at 33% off and the sales tax is 5%?

Step 1.	Change the percent to a decimal.	33% = 0.33	

Step 2. Multiply.

$$
\begin{array}{r}
\$4\ 6 \\
\times\ 0.3\ 3 \\
\hline
1\ 3\ 8 \\
1\ 3\ 8 \\
\hline
\$1\ 5.1\ 8
\end{array}
$$
Amount of savings.

Step 3. The shoes were on sale, so subtract.

$$
\begin{array}{r}
\$4\ 6.0\ 0 \\
-\ 1\ 5.1\ 8 \\
\hline
\$3\ 0.8\ 2
\end{array}
$$
Sale price.

The sales tax is on the actual purchase price.

Step 4. Change the percent to a decimal. 5% = 0.05

Step 5. Multiply.

$$
\begin{array}{r}
\$3\ 0.8\ 2 \\
\times\ 0.0\ 5 \\
\hline
\$1.5\ 4\ 1\ 0
\end{array}
$$
Sales tax.

Step 6. A sales tax increases the price, so add.

$$
\begin{array}{r}
\$3\ 0.8\ 2 \\
+\ \$\ \ 1.5\ 4 \\
\hline
\$3\ 2.3\ 6
\end{array}
$$
Cost.

Practice. Answer these questions. Then compare your answers with those in *Answers and Solutions* on page 103.

1. What is the total price of an item that costs $54.50 and has a sales tax of 6%?

2. If a stove is marked down 30% from its original price of $350, what is the sale price?

STRATEGIES FOR SUCCESS

SOLVING PROBLEMS WITH SEVERAL STEPS

To solve problems you may have to use several steps.

STRATEGY: Break it down.

1. Check to see if there are any key words to help you break the problem down.
2. Figure out what the steps are.
3. Do one step at a time.

Example: Are there any key words in this problem?   What are the different steps?

> Mrs. Crain borrowed $250 from the bank to buy a new stove.   The interest rate is 9% for one year.   How much will she have to pay back at the end of the year?

Key words help you break a problem down into steps.   Key words in this problem are *interest rate* and *how much...pay*.

First find the amount of interest (the amount borrowed times the interest rate).   Notice the hidden step: you have to change the percent to a decimal.

$$9\% = 0.09 \qquad \begin{array}{r} \$2\,5\,0 \\ \times\ 0.0\,9 \\ \hline \$2\,2.5\,0 \end{array}$$

Then find the amount to be paid back (the amount borrowed plus the interest).

$$\begin{array}{r} \$2\,5\,0.0\,0 \\ +\quad 2\,2.5\,0 \\ \hline \$2\,7\,2.5\,0 \end{array}$$

Other key words often found in percent problems are *discount* (the amount a price is reduced) and *sale price* (the price after the discount has been subtracted).

Solve these problems. Use the strategy on page 98.

1. C. J. and the Boys is a country band that plays on weekends. There are four men in the band, and they split all the expenses evenly. They recently bought some new sound equipment priced at $1,232. The store offered a 15% discount for cash purchases. Including the sales tax of 5%, how much did each band member have to pay?

- What are the key words? _____
- What are the different steps? _____
  _____
  _____
  _____

- There is a hidden step. What is it? _____
- What is the answer? _____

2. Ellen and Bruce Grogan have a special savings account for vacations. Ellen deposited $350 into this account and Bruce deposited $565. The interest rate was 6%. How much money was in the account after one year?

- What are the key words? _____
- What are the different steps? _____
  _____
  _____
  _____

- There is a hidden step. What is it? _____
- What is the answer? _____

Check your answers. Reread the problems. Ask yourself if the answers make sense. Look for careless errors in your work such as misplaced decimal points.

Compare your answers with those in *Answers and Solutions* on page 103.

Self-Test

Solve these problems. Put an X next to the correct answer. Then compare your answers with those in *Answers and Solutions* on page 104.

Percent word problems with several steps.

1. Ray's Tire Outlet is having a close-out sale, with 40% off on steel-belted tires. The regular price for a tire is $74.99. What is the sale price? (Use $75 to do your figuring.)
   ____ (1) $45
   ____ (2) $48
   ____ (3) $50
   ____ (4) $55
   ____ (5) $60

2. Bath towels are on sale at 50% off. They regularly cost $7.99 each. How much are they on sale?
   ____ (1) $2.50
   ____ (2) $2.75
   ____ (3) $3.25
   ____ (4) $4.00
   ____ (5) $4.25

3. Block Department Store is having a sale on mirrors. A mirror usually costs $39.99. At 30% off, what is the price of a mirror?
   ____ (1) $27
   ____ (2) $28
   ____ (3) $30
   ____ (4) $35
   ____ (5) $37

4. Carpet sells for $15.99 per square yard. It is on sale for 25% off. What is the sale price of the carpet?
   ____ (1) $12 per sq yd
   ____ (2) $12.50 per sq yd
   ____ (3) $14 per sq yd
   ____ (4) $14.50 per sq yd
   ____ (5) $18 per sq yd

5. Inez earns $47.20 per day. If she receives a pay increase of 12% for outstanding work, how much will she earn? (Round to the nearest cent.)
   ____ (1) $5.66
   ____ (2) $21.86
   ____ (3) $41.54
   ____ (4) $52.86
   ____ (5) $56.64

6. At Hines Store, car batteries usually cost $64.99. The sale price is 23% off the regular price. How much will a battery cost on sale if the sale tax is 5%?

_____ (1) $14.70

_____ (2) $26.25

_____ (3) $47.50

_____ (4) $52.55

_____ (5) $57.75

7. Don is buying a multi-speed fan. It regularly costs $29.99. If he can get it for 33% off, how much will he have to pay with 5% sales tax?

_____ (1) $19.45

_____ (2) $21.00

_____ (3) $21.11

_____ (4) $26.25

_____ (5) $29.40

8. How much interest would a savings account with a balance of $100,000 earn at 11% a year?

_____ (1) $11

_____ (2) $110

_____ (3) $1,100

_____ (4) $11,000

_____ (5) $110,000

9. How much interest would a person pay to borrow $650 for a year at 18%?

_____ (1) $65

_____ (2) $72

_____ (3) $92

_____ (4) $111

_____ (5) $117

10. The original price of a door lock was $14.50. It is on sale for 20% off. If the sales tax is 6%, what will the total cost be?

_____ (1) $10.60

_____ (2) $11.30

_____ (3) $11.60

_____ (4) $12.30

_____ (5) $14.35

11. Rosa weighed 120 pounds. During an illness she lost 5% of her weight. What is her weight now?
_____ (1) 95 lb
_____ (2) 104 lb
_____ (3) 114 lb
_____ (4) 115 lb
_____ (5) 124 lb

12. One year a local railroad company had 450 miles of track in service. By the next year, the miles of tracks had decreased by 3%. How many miles were then in service?
_____ (1) 436.5 miles
_____ (2) 437 miles
_____ (3) 453 miles
_____ (4) 460.5 miles
_____ (5) 463.5 miles

13. Mr. Packard borrowed $5,000 to improve his home. If the interest rate was 9% a year, and he paid the loan back at the end of one year, how much did he pay the bank?
_____ (1) $4,550
_____ (2) $5,045
_____ (3) $5,450
_____ (4) $6,450
_____ (5) $9,500

14. There were 80 cars parked in the parking lot of the ACME Chemical Company. By 6 p.m. 75% of the cars were gone. How many cars were still in the parking lot?
_____ (1) 5 cars
_____ (2) 20 cars
_____ (3) 35 cars
_____ (4) 40 cars
_____ (5) 60 cars

15. Phil bought several items at a Going-Out-Of-Business Sale. Everything in the store was 60% off the marked price. He bought a shirt marked $16.00, a tie marked $6.00, 3 pairs of socks marked $1.50 per pair, and a jacket marked $55.50. The sales tax was 7%. How much did he have to pay for his purchases?
_____ (1) $35.10
_____ (2) $49.20
_____ (3) $52.64
_____ (4) $79.19
_____ (5) $82.00

Answers and Solutions

1. $\frac{10}{100} = \frac{1}{10}$ 2. $\frac{35}{100} = \frac{7}{20}$ 3. $\frac{3}{100}$

4. $\frac{75}{100} = \frac{3}{4}$ 5. $\frac{62}{100} = \frac{31}{50}$ 6. $\frac{50}{100} = \frac{1}{2}$

7. $\frac{95}{100} = \frac{19}{20}$ 8. $\frac{45}{100} = \frac{9}{20}$

9. 37%   10. 2%   11. $66\frac{2}{3}$%

12. 13%   13. 40%   14. 49%

15. 15%   16. 25%

Page 93 Practice

1.
$$
\begin{array}{r}
5\,4 \\
\times\ 0.1 \\
\hline
5.4
\end{array}
$$

2.
$$
\begin{array}{r}
4\,8 \\
\times\ 0.7\,5 \\
\hline
2\,4\,0 \\
3\,3\,6 \\
\hline
3\,6.0\,0
\end{array}
$$

3.
$$
\begin{array}{r}
2\,6.5 \\
\times\ 0.4\,0 \\
\hline
0\,0\,0 \\
1\,0\,6\,0 \\
\hline
1\,0.6\,0\,0
\end{array}
$$

4. $100\% = 1$
$37 \times 1 = 37$

5.
$$
\begin{array}{r}
1\,5\,0 \\
\times\ 0.0\,5 \\
\hline
7.5\,0
\end{array}
$$

6.
$$
\begin{array}{r}
9\,2 \\
\times\ 0.0\,1 \\
\hline
0.9\,2
\end{array}
$$

Page 94 Self-Test

1. (2) 10 hours
$50\% = 0.5$
$$
\begin{array}{r}
2\,0 \\
\times\ 0.5 \\
\hline
1\,0.0
\end{array}
$$

2. (5) 100%
$\frac{8}{8} = 1$
$1 = \frac{100}{100} = 100\%$

3. (4) $592.56
$60\% = 0.60$
$$
\begin{array}{r}
\$9\,8\,7.6\,0 \\
\times\ 0.6\,0 \\
\hline
0\,0\,0\,0\,0 \\
5\,9\,2\,5\,6\,0 \\
\hline
\$5\,9\,2.5\,6\,0\,0
\end{array}
$$

4. (2) $\frac{1}{10}$ $10\% = \frac{10}{100} = \frac{1}{10}$

5. (4) 70%
$$
\begin{array}{r}
1\,0\,0\% \\
-\ 3\,0\% \\
\hline
7\,0\%
\end{array}
$$

Page 95 Self-Test

6. (2) $3.72
$15\% = 0.15$
$$
\begin{array}{r}
\$2\,4.8\,0 \\
\times\ 0.1\,5 \\
\hline
1\,2\,4\,0\,0 \\
2\,4\,8\,0 \\
\hline
\$3.7\,2\,0\,0
\end{array}
$$

7. (1) 81 people
$36\% = 0.36$
$$
\begin{array}{r}
2\,2\,5 \\
\times\ 0.3\,6 \\
\hline
1\,3\,5\,0 \\
6\,7\,5 \\
\hline
8\,1.0\,0
\end{array}
$$

8. (5) 210.1 miles
$55\% = 0.55$
$$
\begin{array}{r}
3\,8\,2 \\
\times\ 0.5\,5 \\
\hline
1\,9\,1\,0 \\
1\,9\,1\,0 \\
\hline
2\,1\,0.1\,0
\end{array}
$$

9. (4) 310 lb
$62\% = 0.62$
$$
\begin{array}{r}
5\,0\,0 \\
\times\ 0.6\,2 \\
\hline
1\,0\,0\,0 \\
3\,0\,0\,0 \\
\hline
3\,1\,0.0\,0
\end{array}
$$

10. (3) $60.00
$15\% = 0.15$
$$
\begin{array}{r}
\$4\,0\,0 \\
\times\ 0.1\,5 \\
\hline
2\,0\,0\,0 \\
4\,0\,0 \\
\hline
\$6\,0.0\,0
\end{array}
$$

Page 97 Practice

1. Total price $57.77
$6\% = 0.06$
$$
\begin{array}{r}
\$5\,4.5\,0 \\
\times\ 0.0\,6 \\
\hline
\$3.2\,7\,0\,0
\end{array}
\qquad
\begin{array}{r}
\$5\,4.5\,0 \\
+\ \ \ \ 3.2\,7 \\
\hline
\$5\,7.7\,7
\end{array}
$$

2. Sale price $245
$30\% = 0.30$
$$
\begin{array}{r}
\$3\,5\,0 \\
\times\ 0.3\,0 \\
\hline
0\,0\,0 \\
1\,0\,5\,0 \\
\hline
\$1\,0\,5.0\,0
\end{array}
\qquad
\begin{array}{r}
\$3\,5\,0 \\
-\ 1\,0\,5 \\
\hline
\$2\,4\,5
\end{array}
$$

Page 98 Strategies For Success

1. • discount; sales tax; each…pay
   • Find the amount of the discount, the sale price, and the sales tax.   Add the sales tax and the sale price to get the total price. Then divide to find the cost per band member.
   • To find the discount and the sales tax you have to change the percent to a decimal.
   • Each band member must pay $274.89.

$15\% = 0.15$
$$
\begin{array}{r}
\$1,2\,3\,2 \\
\times\ 0.1\,5 \\
\hline
6\,1\,6\,0 \\
1\,2\,3\,2 \\
\hline
\$1\,8\,4.8\,0
\end{array}
$$
$$
\begin{array}{r}
\$1,2\,3\,2.0\,0 \\
-\ \ \ 1\,8\,4.8\,0 \\
\hline
\$1,0\,4\,7.2\,0
\end{array}
$$

$5\% = 0.05$
$$
\begin{array}{r}
\$1,0\,4\,7.2\,0 \\
\times\ 0.0\,5 \\
\hline
\$5\,2.3\,6\,0\,0
\end{array}
$$
$$
\begin{array}{r}
\$1,0\,4\,7.2\,0 \\
+\ \ \ \ \ 5\,2.3\,6 \\
\hline
\$1,0\,9\,9.5\,6
\end{array}
$$

$$
\begin{array}{r}
\$\ \ 2\,7\,4.8\,9 \\
4\,\overline{)\$1,0\,9\,9.5\,6} \\
\underline{8}\ \ \ \ \ \ \ \ \ \ \\
2\,9 \\
\underline{2\,8} \\
1\,9 \\
\underline{1\,6} \\
3\,5 \\
\underline{3\,2} \\
3\,6 \\
\underline{3\,6}
\end{array}
$$

2. • interest; how much…money
   • Find the total deposit and the amount of interest.   Add the interest to the deposits.
   • To find the amount of interest you have to change the percent to a decimal.
   • $969.90 is in the account after one year.

$$6\% = 0.06$$

$\begin{array}{r} \$3\ 5\ 0 \\ +\ \ \ 5\ 6\ 5 \\ \hline \$9\ 1\ 5 \end{array}$	$\begin{array}{r} \$9\ 1\ 5 \\ \times\ 0.0\ 6 \\ \hline \$5\ 4.9\ 0 \end{array}$	$\begin{array}{r} \$9\ 1\ 5.0\ 0 \\ +\ \ \ \ 5\ 4.9\ 0 \\ \hline \$9\ 6\ 9.9\ 0 \end{array}$

Page 100   Self-Test

1. (1) $45
$40\% = 0.40$

$$\begin{array}{r} \$7\ 5 \\ \times\ 0.4\ 0 \\ \hline 0\ 0 \\ 3\ 0\ 0 \\ \hline \$3\ 0.0\ 0 \end{array} \qquad \begin{array}{r} \$7\ 5 \\ -\ \ \ 3\ 0 \\ \hline \$4\ 5 \end{array}$$

2. (4) $4.00
$50\% = 0.50$

$$\begin{array}{r} \$8 \\ \times\ 0.5\ 0 \\ \hline 0 \\ 4\ 0 \\ \hline \$4.0\ 0 \end{array} \qquad \begin{array}{r} \$8.0\ 0 \\ -\ \ 4.0\ 0 \\ \hline \$4.0\ 0 \end{array}$$

3. (2) $28
$30\% = 0.30$

$$\begin{array}{r} \$4\ 0 \\ \times\ 0.3\ 0 \\ \hline 0\ 0 \\ 1\ 2\ 0 \\ \hline \$1\ 2.0\ 0 \end{array} \qquad \begin{array}{r} \$4\ 0 \\ -\ \ 1\ 2 \\ \hline \$2\ 8 \end{array}$$

4. (1) $12 per sq yd
$25\% = 0.25$

$$\begin{array}{r} \$1\ 6 \\ \times\ 0.2\ 5 \\ \hline 8\ 0 \\ 3\ 2 \\ \hline \$4.0\ 0 \end{array} \qquad \begin{array}{r} \$1\ 6 \\ -\ \ \ 4 \\ \hline \$1\ 2 \end{array}$$

5. (4) $52.86
$12\% = 0.12$

$$\begin{array}{r} \$4\ 7.2\ 0 \\ \times\ 0.1\ 2 \\ \hline 9\ 4\ 4\ 0 \\ 4\ 7\ 2\ 0 \\ \hline \$5.6\ 6\ 4\ 0 \end{array} \qquad \begin{array}{r} \$4\ 7.2\ 0 \\ +\ \ \ 5.6\ 6 \\ \hline \$5\ 2.8\ 6 \end{array}$$

Page 101   Self-Test

6. (4) $52.55 $23\% = 0.23$ $5\% = 0.05$

$$\begin{array}{r} \$6\ 5 \\ \times\ 0.2\ 3 \\ \hline 1\ 9\ 5 \\ 1\ 3\ 0 \\ \hline \$1\ 4.9\ 5 \end{array} \qquad \begin{array}{r} \$6\ 5.0\ 0 \\ -\ \ 1\ 4.9\ 5 \\ \hline \$5\ 0.0\ 5 \end{array} \qquad \begin{array}{r} \$5\ 0.0\ 5 \\ \times\ 0.0\ 5 \\ \hline 2.5\ 0\ 2\ 5 \end{array}$$

$$\begin{array}{r} \$5\ 0.0\ 5 \\ +\ \ \ 2.5\ 0 \\ \hline \$5\ 2.5\ 5 \end{array}$$

7. (3) $21.11 $33\% = 0.33$ $5\% = 0.05$

$$\begin{array}{r} \$3\ 0 \\ \times\ 0.3\ 3 \\ \hline 9\ 0 \\ 9\ 0 \\ \hline \$9.9\ 0 \end{array} \quad \begin{array}{r} \$3\ 0.0\ 0 \\ -\ \ \ 9.9\ 0 \\ \hline \$2\ 0.1\ 0 \end{array} \quad \begin{array}{r} \$2\ 0.1\ 0 \\ \times\ 0.0\ 5 \\ \hline \$1.0\ 0\ 5\ 0 \end{array} \quad \begin{array}{r} \$2\ 0.1\ 0 \\ +\ \ \ 1.0\ 1 \\ \hline \$2\ 1.1\ 1 \end{array}$$

8. (4) $11,000
$11\% = 0.11$

9. (5) $117
$18\% = 0.18$

$$\begin{array}{r} \$1\ 0\ 0,0\ 0\ 0 \\ \times\ 0.1\ 1 \\ \hline 1\ 0\ 0\ 0\ 0\ 0 \\ 1\ 0\ 0\ 0\ 0\ 0 \\ \hline \$1\ 1,0\ 0\ 0.0\ 0 \end{array} \qquad \begin{array}{r} \$6\ 5\ 0 \\ \times\ 0.1\ 8 \\ \hline 5\ 2\ 0\ 0 \\ 6\ 5\ 0 \\ \hline \$1\ 1\ 7.0\ 0 \end{array}$$

10. (4) $12.30 $20\% = 0.20$ $6\% = 0.06$

$$\begin{array}{r} \$1\ 4.5\ 0 \\ \times\ 0.2\ 0 \\ \hline 0\ 0\ 0\ 0 \\ 2\ 9\ 0\ 0 \\ \hline \$2.9\ 0\ 0\ 0 \end{array} \quad \begin{array}{r} \$1\ 4.5\ 0 \\ -\ \ \ \ 2.9\ 0 \\ \hline \$1\ 1.6\ 0 \end{array} \quad \begin{array}{r} \$1\ 1.6\ 0 \\ \times\ 0.0\ 6 \\ \hline \$0.6\ 9\ 6\ 0 \end{array} \quad \begin{array}{r} \$1\ 1.6\ 0 \\ +\ \ \ \ .7\ 0 \\ \hline \$1\ 2.3\ 0 \end{array}$$

Page 102   Self-Test

11. (3) 114 lb
$5\% = 0.05$

$$\begin{array}{r} 1\ 2\ 0 \\ \times\ 0.0\ 5 \\ \hline 6.0\ 0 \end{array} \qquad \begin{array}{r} 1\ 2\ 0 \\ -\ \ \ \ 6 \\ \hline 1\ 1\ 4 \end{array}$$

12. (1) 436.5 miles
$3\% = 0.03$

$$\begin{array}{r} 4\ 5\ 0 \\ \times\ 0.0\ 3 \\ \hline 1\ 3.5\ 0 \end{array} \qquad \begin{array}{r} 4\ 5\ 0.0 \\ -\ \ 1\ 3.5 \\ \hline 4\ 3\ 6.5 \end{array}$$

13. (3) $5,450
$9\% = 0.09$

$$\begin{array}{r} \$5,0\ 0\ 0 \\ \times\ 0.0\ 9 \\ \hline \$4\ 5\ 0.0\ 0 \end{array} \qquad \begin{array}{r} \$5,0\ 0\ 0 \\ +\ \ \ 4\ 5\ 0 \\ \hline \$5,4\ 5\ 0 \end{array}$$

14. (2) 20 cars
$75\% = 0.75$

$$\begin{array}{r} 8\ 0 \\ \times\ 0.7\ 5 \\ \hline 4\ 0\ 0 \\ 5\ 6\ 0 \\ \hline 6\ 0.0\ 0 \end{array} \qquad \begin{array}{r} 8\ 0 \\ -\ \ 6\ 0 \\ \hline 2\ 0 \end{array}$$

15. (1) $35.10

$$\begin{array}{r} 1\ 0\ 0\% \\ -\ \ \ 6\ 0\% \\ \hline 4\ 0\% \end{array} \qquad 40\% = 0.40$$

$$\begin{array}{r} \$1\ 6.0\ 0 \\ 6.0\ 0 \\ 4.5\ 0 \\ +\ \ 5\ 5.5\ 0 \\ \hline \$8\ 2.0\ 0 \end{array} \qquad \begin{array}{r} \$8\ 2.0\ 0 \\ \times\ 0.4\ 0 \\ \hline 0\ 0\ 0\ 0 \\ 3\ 2\ 8\ 0\ 0 \\ \hline \$3\ 2.8\ 0\ 0\ 0 \end{array}$$

$$\begin{array}{r} \$1.5\ 0 \\ \times\ 3 \\ \hline \$4.5\ 0 \end{array}$$

$7\% = 0.07$

$$\begin{array}{r} \$3\ 2.8\ 0 \\ \times\ 0.0\ 7 \\ \hline \$2.2\ 9\ 6\ 0 \to \$2.30 \end{array} \qquad \begin{array}{r} \$3\ 2.8\ 0 \\ +\ \ \ \ 2.3\ 0 \\ \hline \$3\ 5.1\ 0 \end{array}$$

MEASUREMENT

YOU probably use some kind of measurement every day. You use feet and inches when you measure the height of your children. When you buy carpet or linoleum, you measure a room in square feet. Your doctor weighs you in pounds and ounces. Time is measurement too. Every time you punch out at work, you measure how many hours and minutes you spend on your job.

In this unit, you will learn about units of measurement and their equivalents. You will learn how to figure out and solve problems using measurement.

1. LENGTH

When you build something, you need to take many measurements. Rulers and tape measures are used for measuring length. They are marked off into inches and feet. Sometimes a more exact measurement is needed, so you use the marks that indicate $\frac{1}{2}$ inches, $\frac{1}{4}$ inches, $\frac{1}{8}$ inches and $\frac{1}{16}$ inches.

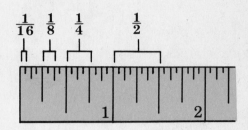

You add or subtract fractions of an inch the same way you add or subtract any other kind of fractions.

$$2 \frac{7}{8} \text{ inches} \qquad 2 \frac{7}{8} \text{ inches}$$
$$- 1 \frac{1}{4} \text{ inches} \qquad - 1 \frac{2}{8} \text{ inches}$$
$$\overline{\qquad\qquad\qquad} \qquad \overline{1 \frac{5}{8} \text{ inches}}$$

Look at the following example using inches and feet. Remember that you can only add or subtract like units of measurement.

Example:

Phil had 2 pieces of lumber. One is 4 feet 8 inches long and the other is 3 feet 7 inches long. How much lumber does he have altogether?

$$
\begin{array}{ll}
4 \text{ feet } 8 \text{ inches} & 4 \text{ feet} \qquad 8 \text{ inches} \\
+ 3 \text{ feet } 7 \text{ inches} & + 3 \text{ feet} \quad + 7 \text{ inches} \\
\hline
& 7 \text{ feet} \qquad 1\,5 \text{ inches} = 8 \text{ feet } 3 \text{ inches}
\end{array}
$$

This answer could be given as 8 feet 3 inches or it could be changed to yards, feet and inches.

$$8 \text{ feet } 3 \text{ inches} = 2 \text{ yards } 2 \text{ feet } 3 \text{ inches}$$

To review equivalent units of measurement, see *For Your Information* on page 12.

When you subtract, you can borrow if necessary.   But remember to borrow a whole unit.

$$\begin{array}{r} 5 \text{ yd } 1 \text{ ft } 6 \text{ in.} \\ - 2 \text{ yd } 2 \text{ ft } 4 \text{ in.} \\ \hline \end{array} \qquad \begin{array}{r} \overset{4}{\cancel{5}} \text{ yd } \overset{4}{\cancel{1}} \text{ ft } 6 \text{ in.} \\ - 2 \text{ yd } 2 \text{ ft } 4 \text{ in.} \\ \hline 2 \text{ yd } 2 \text{ ft } 2 \text{ in.} \end{array}$$

You can easily convert from one unit of measure to another.

Example:

Alice's daughter is 42 inches tall.   What is her height in feet and inches?

You need to find the number of feet in 42 inches.   There are 12 inches in one foot, so you divide 42 by 12.

$$\begin{array}{r} 3 \\ 1\,2\,\overline{)4\,2} \\ 3\,6 \\ \hline 6 \end{array} \qquad 42 \text{ in.} = 3 \text{ ft } 6 \text{ in.}$$

Example:

Mr. Hughes needs 16 yards of molding for the living room of his house.   Molding is sold by the foot.   How many feet does he need?

There are 3 feet in each yard, so multiply the number of yards by 3.

$$\begin{array}{r} 1\,6 \\ \times \ 3 \\ \hline 4\,8 \end{array} \qquad 16 \text{ yd} = 48 \text{ ft}$$

Practice.   Solve these problems.   Then compare your answers with those in *Answers and Solutions* on page 120.

1. $\begin{array}{r} 1 \text{ ft } 4\frac{1}{2} \text{ in.} \\ + 1 \text{ ft } 5 \ \ \text{ in.} \\ \hline \end{array}$

    2. $\begin{array}{r} 6 \text{ ft } 10 \text{ in.} \\ - 4 \text{ ft } \ \ 5 \text{ in.} \\ \hline \end{array}$

    3. $\begin{array}{r} 3 \text{ ft } 6 \ \ \text{ in.} \\ + 1 \text{ ft } 9\frac{1}{2} \text{ in.} \\ \hline \end{array}$

    4. $\begin{array}{r} 4 \text{ ft } 7 \text{ in.} \\ - 1 \text{ ft } 9 \text{ in.} \\ \hline \end{array}$

5. 28 in. = ____ ft ____ in.   6. 95 ft = ____ yd ____ ft   7. 8 ft = ____ in.

S*elf-Test*

Length word problems.

1. Steve Bianca is 6 ft 2 in. tall.   His grandmother is 4 ft 10 in. tall.   How much taller is Mr. Bianca than his grandmother?
   - _____ (1) 8 in.
   - _____ (2) 1 ft 2 in.
   - _____ (3) 1 ft 4 in.
   - _____ (4) 1 ft 8 in.
   - _____ (5) 2 ft 8 in.

2. Bena's kitchen has a sink with a counter on each side.   One counter is 2 ft 3 in. long.   The other is 1 ft 10 in.   How long a piece of formica is needed to cover both counters?
   - _____ (1) 5 in.
   - _____ (2) 2 ft 7 in.
   - _____ (3) 3 ft 7 in.
   - _____ (4) 4 ft 1 in.
   - _____ (5) 5 ft 11 in.

3. Mr. Glatz is remodeling two rooms. He needs 12 feet 8 inches of molding for the first room.   He needs 16 feet 4 inches for the second room.   How many feet of molding should he buy?
   - _____ (1) 12 ft
   - _____ (2) 16 ft
   - _____ (3) 24 ft
   - _____ (4) 28 ft
   - _____ (5) 29 ft

4. Tim Foo is 68″ tall.   How much is that in feet and inches?
   - _____ (1) 4′ 10″
   - _____ (2) 5′ 2″
   - _____ (3) 5′ 4″
   - _____ (4) 5′ 8″
   - _____ (5) 6′ 2″

5. Mrs. Nelson bought 9 yards of fabric to make dish towels.   Each towel requires 27 inches of fabric.   How many towels can be cut from the material?
   - _____ (1) 3 towels
   - _____ (2) 12 towels
   - _____ (3) 16 towels
   - _____ (4) 21 towels
   - _____ (5) 24 towels

6. John needed 108 inches of rope. The store sells rope by the yard. How many yards of rope did he buy?

_____ (1) 2 yd

_____ (2) 3 yd

_____ (3) 6 yd

_____ (4) 8 yd

_____ (5) 10 yd

7. Nora bought 6 yards of cloth. She cut off a piece 2 feet long. How much cloth did she have left?

_____ (1) 4 yd

_____ (2) 4 yd 1 ft

_____ (3) 5 yd

_____ (4) 5 yd 1 ft

_____ (5) 6 yd 1 ft

8. Roland had 5 yards of cord. He used 2 yards 11 inches for his tent. How much cord was left?

_____ (1) 2 yd 2 in.

_____ (2) 2 yd 1 ft 2 in.

_____ (3) 2 yd 2 ft 1 in.

_____ (4) 3 yd 2 in.

_____ (5) 3 yd 3 in.

9. Ruth's back yard has a fence that is 3 feet 6 inches tall. She planted a tree that is 8 feet tall. How much taller is the tree than the fence?

_____ (1) 3 ft 2 in.

_____ (2) 4 ft 6 in.

_____ (3) 5 ft 2 in.

_____ (4) 5 ft 6 in.

_____ (5) 5 ft 8 in.

10. Bill Johnson is buying wood to repair the eaves on three sides of his house. He needs 25 feet on one side, 17 feet on another side, and 5 feet on the third side. What is the total length of wood that he needs to buy?

_____ (1) 15 yd

_____ (2) 15 yd 2 ft

_____ (3) 25 yd 1 ft

_____ (4) 40 yd

_____ (5) 47 yd

2. PERIMETER AND AREA

The distance around the outside of something is its *perimeter*. For example, to find the perimeter of a swimming pool, you add the measurements of the four sides.

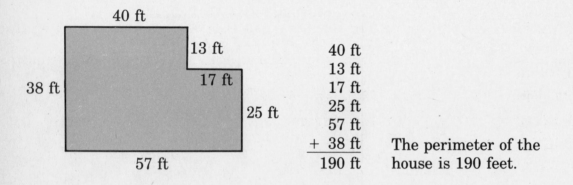

75 ft	
50 ft	
75 ft	
+ 50 ft	The perimeter of the
250 ft	pool is 250 feet.

To find the perimeter of anything, just add the measurements of all the sides.   It can be helpful to draw a picture and write the measurements on the picture when finding the perimeter.

Example:

What is the perimeter of this house?

40 ft	
13 ft	
17 ft	
25 ft	
57 ft	
+ 38 ft	The perimeter of the
190 ft	house is 190 feet.

The *area* is the measurement of the space inside the perimeter.   For example, if you measure the floor of your living room for wall-to-wall carpet or linoleum, you have measured the area of the room.

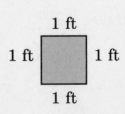

One way to measure area is in square feet.   A square foot is in the shape of a square and measures 1 foot on each side.

How many square feet are there in each figure?   In other words, how many squares 1 ft by 1 ft are there in each figure?   Count them.

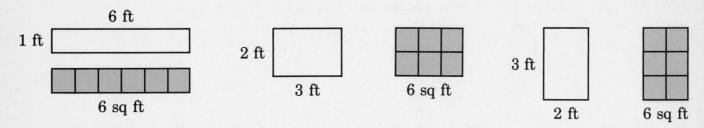

Each of the figures has an area of 6 square feet (6 sq ft).   To find the area of squares and rectangles multiply the length times the width.

Example:

What is the area of a rug 4 feet long and 3 feet wide?

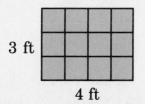

length × width = area
4 feet × 3 feet = 12 square feet

*F*OR YOUR INFORMATION

To measure length or perimeter, use inches, feet, and yards.   To measure area, use square inches, square feet, and square yards.

Practice.   Find the perimeter and area.   Then compare your answers with those in *Answers and Solutions* on page 120.

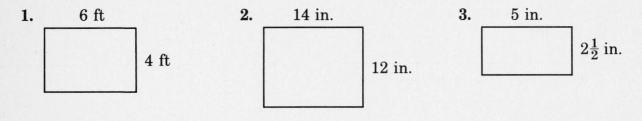

1.   6 ft
4 ft

2.   14 in.
12 in.

3.   5 in.
$2\frac{1}{2}$ in.

$Self$-$Test$

Solve these problems. Put an X next to the correct answer. Then compare your answers with those in *Answers and Solutions* on page 120.

**Word problems on perimeter and area. Some problems have several steps.
Drawing a picture may help you decide what to do first.**

1. Harvey Kimball is building a fence around his cow pasture. The sides of the pasture measure 350′, 400′, 425′, and 375′. How much fencing does he need?

_____ (1) 1,550′

_____ (2) 1,675′

_____ (3) 1,685′

_____ (4) 1,700′

_____ (5) 1,775′

2. Marsha Williams is making a flower bed. It is 10 ft long and 2 ft wide. What is the area of the flower bed?

_____ (1) 12 sq ft

_____ (2) 20 sq ft

_____ (3) 24 sq ft

_____ (4) 40 sq ft

_____ (5) 80 sq ft

3. A square ceiling tile is 1 ft on each side. How many tiles will be needed for the ceiling of a room that measures 9 ft by 12 ft?

_____ (1) 21 tiles

_____ (2) 36 tiles

_____ (3) 108 tiles

_____ (4) 142 tiles

_____ (5) 180 tiles

4. David Santos is putting a new baseboard around the walls of his dining room. The room has two walls that are 9 feet in length and two walls that are 12 feet in length. How many yards of molding should he buy?

_____ (1) 14 yd

_____ (2) 45 yd

_____ (3) 60 yd

_____ (4) 85 yd

_____ (5) 120 yd

5. A rectangular house that measures 24 feet by 60 feet was built on a lot that measures 50 feet by 100 feet. How many square feet of the lot are not covered by the house?

_____ (1) 1,440 sq ft

_____ (2) 3,560 sq ft

_____ (3) 3,660 sq ft

_____ (4) 4,660 sq ft

_____ (5) 5,000 sq ft

6. Mrs. Welch is buying new carpeting for her living room. The room is 5 yards by 3 yards wide. If her carpet costs $10 a square yard, how much will it cost to carpet the room?

____ (1) $15

____ (2) $80

____ (3) $150

____ (4) $160

____ (5) $200

7. A hexagon has 6 equal sides. If each side of a certain hexagon is 3″, what is the perimeter?

____ (1) 3″

____ (2) 6″

____ (3) 12″

____ (4) 15″

____ (5) 18″

8. Mrs. James wants to fence her garden to keep out the rabbits. The garden is $30\frac{3}{4}$ ft long and $14\frac{1}{4}$ ft wide. How much fencing should she buy?

____ (1) 90 ft

____ (2) 102 ft

____ (3) 104 $\frac{3}{4}$ ft

____ (4) 383 $\frac{1}{4}$ ft

____ (5) 438 ft

9. John Paine is replacing the floor in his kitchen. It is $8\frac{1}{2}$ ft long and 6 ft wide. How much linoleum will he need?

____ (1) 17 sq ft

____ (2) 29 sq ft

____ (3) 51 sq ft

____ (4) 58 sq ft

____ (5) 62 sq ft

10. A room in a new school has a floor area of 770 square feet. The length is 35 feet. What is the width?

____ (1) 2.2 ft

____ (2) 22 ft

____ (3) 105 ft

____ (4) 220 ft

____ (5) 735 ft

3. FIGURING AMOUNTS OF TIME

Figuring amounts of time is easy in a problem like this:

Ivan worked on his car from 2 p.m. until 5 p.m. How many hours did he work?

Drawing a picture of a clock and subtracting 2 from 5 gives the answer.

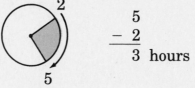

$$\begin{array}{r} 5 \\ -\ 2 \\ \hline 3 \ \text{hours} \end{array}$$

Any problem that includes noon or midnight involves more steps.

Example:

Martha left on an automobile trip at 7:00 in the morning and arrived at 6:00 in the evening. How long did her trip take her?

Step 1. Find the time from 7 a.m. until noon.

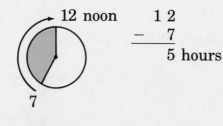

$$\begin{array}{r} 1\ 2 \\ -\ 7 \\ \hline 5 \ \text{hours} \end{array}$$

Step 2. Find the time from noon until 6 p.m.

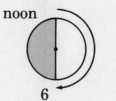

6 hours

Step 3. Add the times.

$$\begin{array}{r} 5 \ \text{hours} \\ +\ 6 \ \text{hours} \\ \hline 11 \ \text{hours} \end{array}$$

Martha's trip took 11 hours.

When subtracting amounts of time, sometimes borrowing and carrying are necessary. Remember that when you borrow 1 hour, you are borrowing 60 minutes.

Example:

Nora punched in on the time clock at Presto Corporation at 6:35 a.m. She punched out at 4:42 p.m. How many hours were recorded on the time clock?

Step 1. Find the amount of time from 6:35 a.m. until noon.

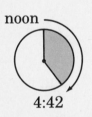

```
    12                    11 hr  60 min
 −   6 hr  35 min       −  6 hr  35 min
                          5 hr  25 min
```

5 hours 25 minutes

Step 2. Find the amount of time from noon to 4:42 p.m.

4 hours 42 minutes

Step 3. Add the times.

```
   5 hr  25 min
 + 4 hr  42 min
   9 hr  67 min  =  10 hr  7 min
```

Nora worked 10 hours 7 minutes.

Practice. Find the amount of time that passed between the two times given. Then compare your answers with those in *Answers and Solutions* on page 121.

1. 4 p.m. and 11 p.m.

2. 10 a.m. and 4:30 p.m.

3. 9:17 a.m. and 4:37 p.m.

STRATEGIES FOR SUCCESS

REVIEWING THE STRATEGIES:
READING, PLANNING, SOLVING, AND CHECKING

Using problem-solving strategies will help you get the correct answer.

READING STRATEGIES: First, read the problem carefully. **Look for key words and identify the important information.**

> Mrs. Jensen had $300 to redecorate her house. She decided to get new wall-to-wall carpet for the living room and linoleum for the dining room. Her living room is 15 ft by 12 ft, and her dining room is 12 ft by 9 ft. She spent $9.50 a square yard for the carpet. How much did she have left for the linoleum?

The key words in this problem are *how much...left*. The important information is the size of Mrs. Jensen's living room (15 ft by 12 ft), the cost of the carpet ($9.50 a square yard), and the $300 she had to spend.

PLANNING STRATEGIES: Next, picture the situation and think the problem through. Break the problem down and look for hidden steps.

The sketch shows the situation. First, find the area of the living room. Then find how much the carpet cost. Notice the hidden step: the size of the living room is in feet, but the cost of the carpet is in square yards.

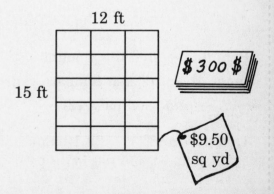

SOLVING STRATEGIES: Choose the operations and do one step at a time.

To change the units of measure from feet to yards, you divide. To find the area, you multiply.

$$3\overline{)12} = 4 \text{ yd} \qquad 3\overline{)15} = 5 \text{ yd}$$

$$\begin{array}{r} 4 \\ \times\ 5 \\ \hline 2\,0 \text{ sq yd} \end{array}$$

To find the cost of the carpet, you multiply. To find out how much she had left, you subtract. (She had $110 left to spend on linoleum.)

$$\begin{array}{r} \$9.5\,0 \\ \times\quad 2\,0 \\ \hline 0\,0\,0 \\ 1\,9\,0\,0 \\ \hline \$1\,9\,0.0\,0 \end{array}$$

$$\begin{array}{r} \$3\,0\,0 \\ -\ 1\,9\,0 \\ \hline \$1\,1\,0 \end{array}$$

CHECKING STRATEGIES: Finally, reread the problem and see if your answer makes sense. Estimate your answer.

Round $9.50 to $10 and estimate the cost of the carpet. Then subtract your estimate from $300. $100 is close to $110.

$$\begin{array}{r} \$1\,0 \\ \times\ 2\,0 \\ \hline 0\,0 \\ 2\,0 \\ \hline \$2\,0\,0 \end{array}$$

$$\begin{array}{r} \$3\,0\,0 \\ -\ 2\,0\,0 \\ \hline \$1\,0\,0 \end{array}$$

Solve this problem. Read, plan, solve, and check.

During a three-week training period, Chris earned $4.00 an hour delivering produce. He worked 35 hours the first week and 40 hours the second and third weeks. The fourth week he worked 37.5 hours at $6.50 an hour. How much more did he earn the fourth week than the first week?

- Underline the important information and draw a sketch.
- What are the key words? _____
- What are the steps in solving the problem? _____

_____

_____

- What's the answer? _____
- What numbers did you round to estimate and check your answer?

_____

Compare your answers with those in *Answers and Solutions* on page 121.

Self-Test

Solve these problems. Put an X next to the correct answer. Then compare your answers with those in *Answers and Solutions* on page 121.

Word problems with time. Some problems have several steps.

1. Mrs. Cleary works at a shoe factory. She punches in at 8 a.m. and punches out at 4 p.m. every day, Monday through Friday. How many hours does she work in one week?

   _____ (1) 20 hr

   _____ (2) 30 hr

   _____ (3) 35 hr

   _____ (4) 40 hr

   _____ (5) 60 hr

2. Tom worked from 10 a.m. until 4 p.m. for five days. He is paid $3.50 per hour. How much was he paid for the week?

   _____ (1) $80

   _____ (2) $95

   _____ (3) $105

   _____ (4) $145

   _____ (5) $205

3. Pearl drives a bus 3 days a week. She begins at 6:30 a.m. and finishes at 2 p.m. She makes $5.00 an hour. How much does she earn a week?

   _____ (1) $102.50

   _____ (2) $105.00

   _____ (3) $107.50

   _____ (4) $112.50

   _____ (5) $187.50

4. Miranda worked an average of 36 hours a week for 12 weeks. Her wage is $4.80 per hour. How much did Miranda earn during the 12 weeks?

   _____ (1) $1,152

   _____ (2) $1,440

   _____ (3) $2,073.60

   _____ (4) $4,147.20

   _____ (5) $6,048

5. Roger Kline, a salesman, parked his car at a parking meter at 9:45 a.m. The parking meter cost 25¢ for 30 minutes. He put 3 quarters in the meter. At what time will he have to return to the car?

   _____ (1) 10:30 a.m.

   _____ (2) 10:45 a.m.

   _____ (3) 10:55 a.m.

   _____ (4) 11:05 a.m.

   _____ (5) 11:15 a.m.

6. Jean works as a salesperson at the North Shore Department Store at $3.50 an hour. On Saturday she punched in at 9:45 a.m. and punched out at 6:15 p.m. How much did she earn that day?
   - _____ (1) $29.75
   - _____ (2) $32.75
   - _____ (3) $35.00
   - _____ (4) $36.25
   - _____ (5) $45.50

7. Willie Brown works weekends as a house parent at a group home for the mentally disabled. He is paid $125 for the weekend. He works from Friday at 6 p.m. until Sunday at 4 p.m. How much does he earn per hour for the weekend? (Round to the nearest cent.)
   - _____ (1) $2.60
   - _____ (2) $2.72
   - _____ (3) $2.98
   - _____ (4) $3.07
   - _____ (5) $3.13

8. Dick Mentz came to work at 7:15 a.m. He left for lunch at 11:00 a.m. and came back to work at noon. He finished work at 4:30 p.m. How many hours did he work?
   - _____ (1) $5\frac{1}{2}$ hr
   - _____ (2) $7\frac{1}{4}$ hr
   - _____ (3) $7\frac{3}{4}$ hr
   - _____ (4) 8 hr
   - _____ (5) $8\frac{1}{4}$ hr

9. Rodrigo arrived at the Eastham Mill at 6:05 in the morning. He took 45 minutes for lunch and left at 4:50 in the afternoon. At $12 an hour, how much did he earn for the day?
   - _____ (1) $105.00
   - _____ (2) $108.50
   - _____ (3) $110.50
   - _____ (4) $120.00
   - _____ (5) $124.00

10. The Hubbard family kept a record of how much time they spent watching television one Saturday:
    9:30 a.m. to 11:00 a.m.
    2:30 p.m. to 5:00 p.m.
    7:30 p.m. to 9:00 p.m.
    How many total hours did they spend watching television?
    - _____ (1) 4 hr 30 min
    - _____ (2) 5 hr 30 min
    - _____ (3) 10 hr 15 min
    - _____ (4) 10 hr 30 min
    - _____ (5) 11 hr 55 min

Answers and Solutions

Page 107   Practice

1.   1 ft 4 $\frac{1}{2}$ in.
  + 1 ft 5   in.
  ‾‾‾‾‾‾‾‾‾‾‾‾
  2 ft 9 $\frac{1}{2}$ in.

2.   6 ft 10 in.
  − 4 ft   5 in.
  ‾‾‾‾‾‾‾‾‾‾‾‾
  2 ft   5 in.

3.   3 ft   6   in.
  + 1 ft   9 $\frac{1}{2}$ in.
  ‾‾‾‾‾‾‾‾‾‾‾‾‾‾
  4 ft 15 $\frac{1}{2}$ in. = 5 ft 3 $\frac{1}{2}$ in.

4.   4 ft 7 in. =   3 ft 19 in.
  − 1 ft 9 in. = − 1 ft   9 in.
  ‾‾‾‾‾‾‾‾‾‾‾‾‾‾‾‾‾‾‾‾‾‾‾‾‾‾
                  2 ft 10 in.

5. 2 ft 4 in.   **6.** 31 yd 2 ft   **7.** 96 in.

```
       2           3 1            1 2
  12)2 8        3)9 5          ×   8
     2 4          9            ‾‾‾‾‾
   ‾‾‾          ‾‾             9 6
     4            5
                  3
                  ‾
                  2
```

Page 108   Self-Test

1. (3) 1 ft 4 in.

     6 ft   2 in. =   5 ft 14 in.
   − 4 ft 10 in. = − 4 ft 10 in.
   ‾‾‾‾‾‾‾‾‾‾‾‾‾‾‾‾‾‾‾‾‾‾‾‾‾‾‾‾‾
                     1 ft   4 in.

2. (4) 4 ft 1 in.

     2 ft   3 in.
   + 1 ft 10 in.
   ‾‾‾‾‾‾‾‾‾‾‾‾‾
     3 ft 13 in. = 4 ft 1 in.

3. (5) 29 ft

     12 ft   8 in.
   + 16 ft   4 in.
   ‾‾‾‾‾‾‾‾‾‾‾‾‾‾
     28 ft 12 in. = 29 ft

4. (4) 5′8″   **5.** (2) 12 towels   1 yd = 36 in.
   1′ = 12″

```
                   3 6            1 2
         5       ×   8        27)3 2 4
  12)6 8         ‾‾‾‾‾          2 7
    6 0         3 2 4          ‾‾‾
    ‾‾‾                         5 4
      8                         5 4
                               ‾‾‾
```

Page 109   Self-Test

6. (2) 3 yd
   1 yd = 36 in.

```
                    3
           36)1 0 8
              1 0 8
```

7. (4) 5 yd 1 ft

       6 yd   =   5 yd 3 ft
   −   2 ft = −   2 ft
   ‾‾‾‾‾‾‾‾‾‾‾‾‾‾‾‾‾‾‾‾‾‾‾‾‾‾‾‾
                    5 yd 1 ft

8. (3) 2 yd 2 ft 1 in.

       5 yd   =   4 yd 2 ft 12 in.
   − 2 yd 11 in.   = − 2 yd   11 in.
   ‾‾‾‾‾‾‾‾‾‾‾‾‾‾‾‾‾‾‾‾‾‾‾‾‾‾‾‾‾‾‾‾‾‾‾
                        2 yd 2 ft   1 in.

9. (2) 4 ft 6 in.

       8 ft   =   7 ft 12 in.
   − 3 ft 6 in.   = − 3 ft   6 in.
   ‾‾‾‾‾‾‾‾‾‾‾‾‾‾‾‾‾‾‾‾‾‾‾‾‾‾‾‾‾‾
                        4 ft   6 in.

10. (2) 15 yd 2 ft

```
       2 5 ft            1 5
       1 7 ft        3)4 7
     +   5 ft          3
     ‾‾‾‾‾‾‾          ‾‾‾
       4 7 ft          1 7
                       1 5
                       ‾‾‾
                         2
```

Page 111   Practice

1. perimeter = 6 + 4 + 6 + 4 = 20 ft
   area = 6 × 4 = 24 sq ft

2. perimeter = 14 + 12 + 14 + 12 = 52 in.
   area = 14 × 12 = 168 sq in.

3. perimeter = 5 + 2 $\frac{1}{2}$ + 5 + 2 $\frac{1}{2}$ = 15 in.
   area = 5 × 2 $\frac{1}{2}$ = 12 $\frac{1}{2}$ sq in.

Page 112   Self-Test

1. (1) 1,550′

```
       3 5 0
       4 0 0
       4 2 5
     + 3 7 5
     ‾‾‾‾‾‾‾
     1,5 5 0
```

2. (2) 20 sq ft   ⬚ 10 ft   2 ft

```
       1 0
     ×   2
     ‾‾‾‾‾
       2 0
```

3. (3) 108 tiles   ⬚ 12 ft   9 ft

```
       1 2
     ×   9
     ‾‾‾‾‾
     1 0 8
```

4. (1) 14 yd

12 ft [ ] 9 ft

$$\begin{array}{r}1\,2\\9\\1\,2\\+\quad9\\\hline4\,2\end{array}\qquad 3\overline{)42}\;^{14}$$

5. (2) 3,560 sq ft

100 ft
60 ft
24 ft   50 ft

$$\begin{array}{r}2\,4\\\times\;6\,0\\\hline1,4\,4\,0\end{array}\qquad\begin{array}{r}1\,0\,0\\\times\;\;5\,0\\\hline5,0\,0\,0\end{array}\qquad\begin{array}{r}5,0\,0\,0\\-\;1,4\,4\,0\\\hline3,5\,6\,0\end{array}$$

Page 113   Self-Test

6. (3) $150

5 yd [ ] 3 yd

$$\begin{array}{r}5\\\times\;3\\\hline1\,5\end{array}\qquad\begin{array}{r}1\,5\\\times\;\$1\,0\\\hline\$1\,5\,0\end{array}$$

7. (5) 18″

3″ 3″ 3″ 3″ 3″

$$\begin{array}{r}3\\\times\;6\\\hline1\,8\end{array}$$

8. (1) 90 ft

$30\frac{3}{4}$ [ ] $14\frac{1}{4}$

$$\begin{array}{r}3\,0\frac{3}{4}\\1\,4\frac{1}{4}\\3\,0\frac{3}{4}\\+\;1\,4\frac{1}{4}\\\hline8\,8\frac{8}{4}=90\end{array}$$

9. (3) 51 sq ft

$8\frac{1}{2}$ ft [ ] 6 ft

$$8\frac{1}{2}=8.5\qquad\begin{array}{r}8.5\\\times\;6\\\hline51.0\end{array}$$

10. (2) 22 ft

770 sq ft   35 ft

$$35\overline{)770}\;^{22}\begin{array}{r}\\7\,0\\\hline7\,0\\7\,0\end{array}$$

Page 115   Practice

1. 7 hours

$$\begin{array}{r}1\,1\\-\;4\\\hline7\end{array}$$

2.

$$\begin{array}{r}1\,2\\-\,1\,0\\\hline2\end{array}\qquad\begin{array}{r}2\;\text{hr}\\+\;4\;\text{hr}\;30\;\text{min}\\\hline6\;\text{hr}\;30\;\text{min}\end{array}$$

3.

$$\begin{array}{rcl}12\;\text{hr}&=&11\;\text{hr}\;60\;\text{min}\\-\;9\;\text{hr}\;17\;\text{min}&=&-\;9\;\text{hr}\;17\;\text{min}\\\hline&&2\;\text{hr}\;43\;\text{min}\end{array}$$

$$\begin{array}{r}2\;\text{hr}\;43\;\text{min}\\+\;4\;\text{hr}\;37\;\text{min}\\\hline6\;\text{hr}\;80\;\text{min}=7\;\text{hr}\;20\;\text{min}\end{array}$$

Page 117   Strategies For Success

- $4.00 an hour; 35 hours the first week; fourth week…37.5 hours at $6.50 an hour

1st week — 35 hr	4th week — 37.5 hr
@ $4.00	@ $6.50

- how much more…earn

- First multiply $4 times 35 hours.   This is how much he earned in the first week.   Then multiply $6.50 times 37.5 hours.   This is how much he earned the fourth week.   Next, subtract the amount he earned the first week from the amount he earned the fourth week.

- He earned $103.75 more the fourth week.

$$\begin{array}{r}\$4.0\,0\\\times\;3\,5\\\hline2\,0\,0\,0\\1\,2\,0\,0\\\hline\$1\,4\,0.0\,0\end{array}\quad\begin{array}{r}\$6.5\,0\\\times\;3\,7.5\\\hline3\,2\,5\,0\\4\,5\,5\,0\\1\,9\,5\,0\\\hline\$2\,4\,3.7\,5\,0\end{array}\quad\begin{array}{r}\$2\,4\,3.7\,5\\-\;1\,4\,0.0\,0\\\hline\$1\,0\,3.7\,5\end{array}$$

- He earned $103.75 more the fourth week.

- 35; $6.50; 37.5

$$\$4\times40=\$160\qquad\begin{array}{r}\$2\,8\,0\\-\;1\,6\,0\\\hline\$1\,2\,0\end{array}$$
$$\$7\times40=\$280$$

Page 118   Self-Test

1. (4) 40 hr

$$\begin{array}{r}1\,2\\-\;8\\\hline4\end{array}\qquad\begin{array}{r}4\\+\,4\\\hline8\end{array}\qquad\begin{array}{r}8\\\times\;5\\\hline4\,0\end{array}$$

2. (3) $105

$$\begin{array}{r}1\,2\\-\,1\,0\\\hline2\end{array}\quad\begin{array}{r}4\\+\,2\\\hline6\end{array}\quad\begin{array}{r}6\\\times\,5\\\hline3\,0\end{array}\quad\begin{array}{r}\$3.5\,0\\\times\;3\,0\\\hline\$1\,0\,5.0\,0\end{array}$$

3. (4) $112.50

$$\begin{array}{rcl}12\;\text{hr}&=&11\;\text{hr}\;60\;\text{min}\\-\;6\;\text{hr}\;30\;\text{min}&=&-\;6\;\text{hr}\;30\;\text{min}\\\hline&&5\;\text{hr}\;30\;\text{min}\end{array}$$

```
  5 hr   30 min
+ 2 hr
  7 hr   30 min
```

```
   7 hr   30 min
   7 hr   30 min
+  7 hr   30 min
  21 hr   90 min  =  22 hr  30 min
                  =  22½ hr = 22.5 hr
```

```
        2 2.5
     × $5.0 0
  $1 1 2.5 0 0
```

4. (3) $2,073.60

```
    3 6            $4.8 0
  × 1 2          ×  4 3 2
    7 2              9 6 0
    3 6            1 4 4 0
  4 3 2           1 9 2 0
                $2,0 7 3.6 0
```

5. (5) 11:15 a.m.

```
    3 0
  ×  3
    9 0  min = 1 hr 30 min
```

```
   9 hr   45 min
+  1 hr   30 min
  10 hr   75 min  =  11 hr  15 min
```

Page 119   Self-Test

6. (1) $29.75

```
   12 hr          =    11 hr  60 min
 −  9 hr  45 min  =  −  9 hr  45 min
                       2 hr  15 min
```

```
   2 hr   15 min
+  6 hr   15 min
   8 hr   30 min  =  8½ hr = 8.5 hr
```

```
   $3.5 0
  ×  8.5
   1 7 5 0
   2 8 0 0
  $2 9.7 5 0
```

7. (2) $2.72

```
Friday 6 p.m. to
  Saturday 6 p.m.      =     24 hr
Saturday 6 p.m. to
  Sunday 6 a.m.        =     12 hr
Sunday 6 a.m. to noon  =      6 hr
Sunday noon to 4 p.m.  =  +   4 hr
                            46 hr
```

```
          2.7 1 7  →  $2.72
  4 6 ) $1 2 5.0 0 0
         9 2
         3 3 0
         3 2 2
           8 0
           4 6
           3 4 0
           3 2 2
             1 8
```

8. (5) 8¼ hr

```
   11 hr          =    10 hr  60 min
 −  7 hr  15 min  =  −  7 hr  15 min
                       3 hr  45 min
```

```
   3 hr   45 min
+  4 hr   30 min
   7 hr   75 min  =  8 hr 15 min
                  =  8¼ hr
```

9. (4) $120

```
   12 hr          =    11 hr  60 min
 −  6 hr   5 min  =  −  6 hr   5 min
                       5 hr  55 min
```

```
   5 hr    55 min
+  4 hr    50 min
   9 hr   105 min
```

```
   9 hr   105 min          $1 2
 −         45 min        × 1 0
   9 hr    60 min = 10 hr  $1 2 0
```

10. (2) 5 hr 30 min

```
   11 hr   0 min  =    10 hr  60 min
 −  9 hr  30 min  =  −  9 hr  30 min
                       1 hr  30 min
```

```
   5 hr   0 min   =    4 hr  60 min
 −  2 hr  30 min  =  −  2 hr  30 min
                       2 hr  30 min
```

```
   9 hr   0 min   =    8 hr  60 min
 −  7 hr  30 min  =  −  7 hr  30 min
                       1 hr  30 min
```

```
Total:   1 hr   30 min
         2 hr   30 min
      +  1 hr   30 min
         4 hr   90 min  =  5 hr 30 min
```

Check What You've Learned

Check What You've Learned will give you an idea of how well you've learned the math skills and problem-solving strategies in this book. This test consists of 36 word problems similar to those on the GED Test.

Read each problem carefully. Using the space on the page or another piece of paper, solve the problem. Then put an X next to the correct answer. There is no time limit.

1. Greg Talcott is paid by the hour for carpentry work. He worked 7 hours each day for four days on one job. How many hours did he work on that job altogether?

_____ (1) 7 hr

_____ (2) 11 hr

_____ (3) 17 hr

_____ (4) 28 hr

_____ (5) 35 hr

2. For Halloween, Mrs. Ravitch bought $\frac{1}{2}$ lb of candy corn, $\frac{3}{4}$ lb of chocolate-covered raisins, and 1 lb of chocolate kisses. How much candy did she buy altogether?

_____ (1) $1\frac{1}{4}$ lb

_____ (2) $1\frac{1}{2}$ lb

_____ (3) 2 lb

_____ (4) $2\frac{1}{4}$ bl

_____ (5) $2\frac{1}{2}$ lb

3. Mr. Orozco bought 6 gallons of paint to repaint 3 rooms in his home. He used 2 gallons to paint the living room, $1\frac{3}{8}$ gallons to paint the dining room, and $\frac{7}{8}$ gallon to paint the hall. How much paint did he have left?

_____ (1) $1\frac{1}{2}$ gallons

_____ (2) $1\frac{3}{4}$ gallons

_____ (3) $3\frac{1}{4}$ gallons

_____ (4) $4\frac{1}{2}$ gallons

_____ (5) $4\frac{3}{8}$ gallons

4. Mrs. Delgado's son wants to go to summer camp for 2 weeks in August. Camp costs $155.50 a week. His grandparents gave him $50 as a birthday present, and he plans to earn the rest of the money himself. How much money must he earn to go to camp?

_____ (1) $105.50

_____ (2) $161.00

_____ (3) $211.00

_____ (4) $211.50

_____ (5) $261.00

5. Mr. Stimple ordered several items from a camping equipment catalog. He ordered a fishing pole for $115.00, a canoe chair for $18.00, a tent for $145.50, and 2 folding cots for $29.00 each. The sales tax was 5%. How much was his total bill? (Round to the nearest cent.)

____ (1) $303.35

____ (2) $336.50

____ (3) $353.33

____ (4) $370.15

____ (5) $403.80

6. Mrs. Willis pays her oldest daughter Marta $2.00 an hour to baby-sit for the younger children. Last week, Marta baby-sat on Monday and Tuesday from 4:30 p.m. to 6:30 p.m., on Wednesday from 3:15 p.m. to 6 p.m., and on Thursday from 3:30 p.m. to 7:45 p.m. How much does Mrs. Willis owe Marta?

____ (1) $20

____ (2) $22

____ (3) $24

____ (4) $26

____ (5) $28

7. Maria Juarez works part time as a bank teller. Last week, she worked 3 hours on Monday, 6 hours on Friday, and 5 hours on Saturday. How many hours did she work last week?

____ (1) 9 hr

____ (2) 11 hr

____ (3) 14 hr

____ (4) 15 hr

____ (5) 16 hr

8. Wendy Perkins is a florist. She uses 11 carnations for one of her most popular arrangements. She received a shipment of 506 carnations. How many arrangements can she make with those carnations?

____ (1) 41 arrangements

____ (2) 43 arrangements

____ (3) 46 arrangements

____ (4) 49 arrangements

____ (5) 50 arrangements

9. Melinda bought $9\frac{3}{4}$ yd of fabric on sale. She sold her neighbor $5\frac{1}{3}$ yd of the fabric. How much fabric did she have left?

____ (1) $3\frac{1}{4}$ yd

____ (2) $3\frac{1}{3}$ yd

____ (3) $3\frac{5}{12}$ yd

____ (4) $4\frac{1}{3}$ yd

____ (5) $4\frac{5}{12}$ yd

10. One weekend, Mr. Bell drove 50.2 miles to a lake to go fishing. After he had fished for several hours, he drove 13.7 miles to a friend's house. Then he drove 67.8 miles home. How many miles did he drive altogether?

_____ (1) 63.9 miles

_____ (2) 81.5 miles

_____ (3) 118.0 miles

_____ (4) 131.7 miles

_____ (5) 141.7 miles

11. Three waiters pool their tips and divide the amount among them. One evening they earned $25.50, $19.90, and $40.40. How much was each person's share?

_____ (1) $28.57

_____ (2) $28.58

_____ (3) $28.60

_____ (4) $28.61

_____ (5) $28.65

12. For a business trip, Ms. Kline bought some new clothes. She bought a raincoat priced at $119.50 which was on sale for 25% off. She also bought a dress for $79.50, a sweater for $29.75, and a pair of slacks for $36.00. What was the cost of the clothing including the sales tax of 7%? (Round to the nearest cent.)

_____ (1) $234.87

_____ (2) $246.61

_____ (3) $251.31

_____ (4) $255.59

_____ (5) $299.65

13. Marvin Hendrick works at the Eastern Paper Mill from 7:30 a.m. to 3:30 p.m. He has a half hour for lunch. Not including lunch, how many hours does he work each day?

_____ (1) 3 hr 30 min

_____ (2) 4 hr 30 min

_____ (3) 7 hr 30 min

_____ (4) 8 hr

_____ (5) 8 hr 30 min

14. A restaurant served 253 dinners on Friday night and 302 dinners on Saturday night. How many more dinners were served on Saturday than on Friday?

_____ (1) 41 dinners

_____ (2) 49 dinners

_____ (3) 53 dinners

_____ (4) 55 dinners

_____ (5) 61 dinners

15. On weekends, Ralph Medina earns extra money using his truck to help people move. He charges $15 an hour during the day and $18 an hour at night. Last weekend he worked 4 hours on Friday night and 10 hours on Saturday during the day. How much did he earn altogether?

_____ (1) $72

_____ (2) $84

_____ (3) $150

_____ (4) $172

_____ (5) $222

16. Ms. King has 3 nieces. She bought each of them $\frac{1}{2}$ lb of macadamia nuts as a souvenir from Hawaii. How many pounds of macadamia nuts did she buy?

_____ (1) $\frac{1}{2}$ lb

_____ (2) 1 lb

_____ (3) $1\frac{1}{2}$ lb

_____ (4) 2 lb

_____ (5) $3\frac{1}{2}$ lb

17. Eric bought a pair of shoes that cost $63.27. He paid $21 down and the rest the following Friday. How much did he pay on Friday?

_____ (1) $42.27

_____ (2) $44.27

_____ (3) $45.27

_____ (4) $82.27

_____ (5) $84.27

18. Janet Miller had $225.78 in her checking account and $807.59 in her savings account. On Tuesday night she wrote two checks: one for $29.37 and one for $15.00. Later in the week she deposited $81.12 in her checking account. What was the balance in her checking account at the end of the week?

_____ (1) $181.41

_____ (2) $191.05

_____ (3) $191.41

_____ (4) $262.53

_____ (5) $343.65

19. A neighborhood group wants to fence in a vacant lot and start a community garden. The lot is 250 ft by 110 ft. If the fence goes all the way around the lot, how many feet of fencing are needed?

_____ (1) 360 ft

_____ (2) 440 ft

_____ (3) 720 ft

_____ (4) 920 ft

_____ (5) 1,000 ft

20. The Scrantons' patio is 9 ft by 12 ft. They want to replace the concrete with tiles which are 1 foot square. How many tiles will they need to buy?

____ (1) 12 tiles

____ (2) 21 tiles

____ (3) 36 tiles

____ (4) 98 tiles

____ (5) 108 tiles

21. Ms. Woo earned $15,125 last year. She paid $3,075 in taxes. How much money did she have left after taxes?

____ (1) $12,050

____ (2) $12,155

____ (3) $17,050

____ (4) $18,000

____ (5) $18,200

22. For 52 weeks Jerry Reilly spent $5 each week on lottery tickets. During that time he won $160. How much more did he spend than he won?

____ (1) $100

____ (2) $160

____ (3) $260

____ (4) $310

____ (5) $360

23. Al Rodgers jogs on a track that is $\frac{3}{8}$ of a mile. How many times must he run around the track to jog 3 miles?

____ (1) $1\frac{1}{8}$ times

____ (2) 2 times

____ (3) 7 times

____ (4) $7\frac{2}{3}$ times

____ (5) 8 times

24. A group of twelve friends went out to lunch. Everyone ordered the lunch special for $5.95. What was the total cost of the lunch specials?

____ (1) $17.85

____ (2) $17.95

____ (3) $70.40

____ (4) $71.40

____ (5) $107.85

25. At a company located in the suburbs, 27% of the employees participate in a car pool. What percent of the employees do not participate in a car pool?

_____ (1) 73%

_____ (2) 83%

_____ (3) 93%

_____ (4) 97.3%

_____ (5) 127%

26. Mr. Barr wants to carpet the family room in his house. The room is 15 ft by 15 ft. How many square yards of carpeting does he need to buy?

_____ (1) 25 sq yd

_____ (2) 50 sq yd

_____ (3) 75 sq yd

_____ (4) 150 sq yd

_____ (5) 225 sq yd

27. One year ago, Angie bought a used car with 32,557 miles on it. She has driven the car 12,260 miles. How many miles are on the car now?

_____ (1) 20,297 miles

_____ (2) 20,317 miles

_____ (3) 34,717 miles

_____ (4) 44,807 miles

_____ (5) 44,817 miles

28. Phil Bass is a letter carrier with a rural delivery route. During one week he drives 288 miles. His car gets 18 miles per gallon. How many gallons of gasoline does he use in a week?

_____ (1) 15 gallons

_____ (2) 16 gallons

_____ (3) 17 gallons

_____ (4) 18 gallons

_____ (5) 19 gallons

29. During the summer, Mr. and Mrs. Lapp sell fruit and vegetables at a roadside stand. One Saturday, they had 100 pounds of fresh peas which they divided into $2\frac{1}{2}$-pound packages. That morning, they sold $\frac{2}{5}$ of the packages of peas. How many packages did they have left to sell in the afternoon?

_____ (1) 16 packages

_____ (2) 20 packages

_____ (3) 24 packages

_____ (4) 30 packages

_____ (5) 32 packages

30. Laura, April, Suzanne, and Vanessa decided to buy a stroller as a shower present for a friend who was expecting a baby. The stroller cost $79.88. How much was each person's share of the cost?

_____ (1) $19.97

_____ (2) $19.99

_____ (3) $20.97

_____ (4) $39.94

_____ (5) $39.95

31. In a survey of popular ice cream flavors, 34% of the people asked said that vanilla was their favorite flavor. If 250 people were surveyed, how many preferred vanilla?

_____ (1) 80 people

_____ (2) 85 people

_____ (3) 125 people

_____ (4) 206 people

_____ (5) 216 people

32. Frank Sakis sells plants and potting soil at flea markets on the weekends. One week he bought 300 pounds of potting soil mixture. On Saturday he sold 125 pounds of the potting soil and on Sunday he sold 87 pounds. How many pounds of potting soil were left?

_____ (1) 82 pounds

_____ (2) 88 pounds

_____ (3) 112 pounds

_____ (4) 202 pounds

_____ (5) 212 pounds

33. Four people shared a pizza. Each person ate the same amount. How much of the pizza did each person eat?

_____ (1) $\frac{1}{12}$ of the pizza

_____ (2) $\frac{1}{6}$ of the pizza

_____ (3) $\frac{1}{4}$ of the pizza

_____ (4) $\frac{1}{3}$ of the pizza

_____ (5) $\frac{1}{2}$ of the pizza

34. George Romero earned $18,000 last year. He paid $\frac{1}{4}$ of his income in taxes. How much did he have left after taxes?

_____ (1) $4,500

_____ (2) $5,000

_____ (3) $9,500

_____ (4) $12,500

_____ (5) $13,500

35. Quick Start Auto Repair charges $25 an hour for labor. Two mechanics worked repairing one car. One mechanic worked 3.5 hours and the other worked 5.25 hours. The parts for the car cost $169.70. How much should be charged for labor?

_____ (1) $8.75

_____ (2) $87.50

_____ (3) $187.50

_____ (4) $218.75

_____ (5) $388.45

36. Ms. Farrell bought a suit priced at $155.00. It was on sale for 30% off. How much did she pay for the suit?

_____ (1) $46.49

_____ (2) $46.50

_____ (3) $108.49

_____ (4) $108.50

_____ (5) $150.35

When you finish the test, compare your answers with those in _Answers and Solutions_ on page 132. Then complete the chart on page 131 by checking the numbers of the problems you got wrong.

SKILL REVIEW CHART

The chart will show you which math skills you should go back and review. Reread each problem you got wrong. Then look at the appropriate sections of the book for help in figuring out the right answers.

SKILLS	TEST QUESTIONS	STRATEGIES FOR SUCCESS
The test, like this book, focuses on the skills below.	Check (✔) the problems you got wrong.	Review what you learned in this book. Figure out why your answers are wrong.
Addition and Subtraction of Whole Numbers	___ 7 ___ 14 ___ 21 ___ 27 ___ 32	See pages 12–13 STRATEGIES FOR SUCCESS ● Choosing the Operation
Multiplication and Division of Whole Numbers	___ 1 ___ 8 ___ 15 ___ 22 ___ 28	See pages 26–27 STRATEGIES FOR SUCCESS ● Making a Plan
Solving Problems that Involve Fractions	___ 2 ___ 3 ___ 9 ___ 16 ___ 23 ___ 29 ___ 33 ___ 34	See pages 44–45 STRATEGIES FOR SUCCESS ● Solving Problems with a Hidden Step
Solving Problems that Involve Decimals	___ 4 ___ 10 ___ 11 ___ 17 ___ 18 ___ 24 ___ 30 ___ 35	See pages 80–81 STRATEGIES FOR SUCCESS ● Making Problems Easier to Work With
Solving Problems that Involve Percent	___ 5 ___ 12 ___ 25 ___ 31 ___ 36	See pages 98–99 STRATEGIES FOR SUCCESS ● Solving Problems with Several Steps
Solving Problems that Involve Measurement	___ 6 ___ 13 ___ 19 ___ 20 ___ 26	See pages 116–117 STRATEGIES FOR SUCCESS ● Reading, Planning, Solving, and Checking

Answers and Solutions

1. (4) 28 hr

$$\begin{array}{r} 7 \\ \times\ 4 \\ \hline 2\ 8 \end{array}$$

2. (4) $2\frac{1}{4}$ lb

$$\begin{aligned} \tfrac{1}{2} &= & \tfrac{2}{4} \\ \tfrac{3}{4} &= & \tfrac{3}{4} \\ +\ 1\ &=\ & +\ 1 \\ \hline & & 1\tfrac{5}{4} = 2\tfrac{1}{4} \end{aligned}$$

3. (2) $1\frac{3}{4}$ gallons

$$\begin{array}{r} 2 \\ 1\tfrac{3}{8} \\ +\ \ \tfrac{7}{8} \\ \hline 3\tfrac{10}{8} \end{array} = 4\tfrac{1}{4} \qquad \begin{array}{r} 6 \\ -\ 4\tfrac{1}{4} \\ \hline 1\tfrac{3}{4} \end{array}$$

4. (5) $261.00

$$\begin{array}{r} \$1\ 5\ 5.5\ 0 \\ \times\ 2 \\ \hline \$3\ 1\ 1.0\ 0 \end{array} \qquad \begin{array}{r} \$3\ 1\ 1.0\ 0 \\ -\ \ \ 5\ 0.0\ 0 \\ \hline \$2\ 6\ 1.0\ 0 \end{array}$$

5. (3) $353.33

$$\begin{array}{r} \$1\ 1\ 5.0\ 0 \\ 1\ 8.0\ 0 \\ 1\ 4\ 5.5\ 0 \\ 2\ 9.0\ 0 \\ +\ \ \ \ 2\ 9.0\ 0 \\ \hline \$3\ 3\ 6.5\ 0 \end{array}$$

$$5\% = 0.05$$

$$\begin{array}{r} \$3\ 3\ 6.5\ 0 \\ \times\ 0.0\ 5 \\ \hline \$1\ 6.8\ 2\ 5\ 0 \end{array} \to \$16.83$$

$$\begin{array}{r} \$3\ 3\ 6.5\ 0 \\ +\ \ \ \ 1\ 6.8\ 3 \\ \hline \$3\ 5\ 3.3\ 3 \end{array}$$

6. (2) $22   4:30 p.m. – 6:30 p.m.

$$\begin{array}{r} 6\ \text{hr}\ 30\ \text{min} \\ -\ 4\ \text{hr}\ 30\ \text{min} \\ \hline 2\ \text{hr} \end{array}$$

3:15 p.m. – 6:00 p.m.

$$\begin{array}{r} 6\ \text{hr} \\ -\ 3\ \text{hr}\ 15\ \text{min} \\ \hline \end{array} \qquad \begin{array}{r} 5\ \text{hr}\ 60\ \text{min} \\ -\ 3\ \text{hr}\ 15\ \text{min} \\ \hline 2\ \text{hr}\ 45\ \text{min} \end{array}$$

3:30 p.m. – 7:45 p.m.

$$\begin{array}{r} 7\ \text{hr}\ 45\ \text{min} \\ -\ 3\ \text{hr}\ 30\ \text{min} \\ \hline 4\ \text{hr}\ 15\ \text{min} \end{array}$$

$$\begin{array}{r} 2\ \text{hr} \\ 2\ \text{hr} \\ 2\ \text{hr}\ 45\ \text{min} \\ +\ 4\ \text{hr}\ 15\ \text{min} \\ \hline 10\ \text{hr}\ 60\ \text{min} \end{array} = 11\ \text{hr} \qquad \begin{array}{r} 11 \\ \times\ 2 \\ \hline \$22 \end{array}$$

7. (3) 14 hr

$$\begin{array}{r} 3 \\ 6 \\ +\ 5 \\ \hline 1\ 4 \end{array}$$

8. (3) 46 arrangements

$$\begin{array}{r} 4\ 6 \\ 1\ 1\ \overline{)\ 5\ 0\ 6} \\ 4\ 4 \\ \hline 6\ 6 \\ 6\ 6 \\ \hline \end{array}$$

9. (5) $4\frac{5}{12}$ yd

$$\begin{aligned} 9\tfrac{3}{4} &= & 9\tfrac{9}{12} \\ -\ 5\tfrac{1}{3} &= & -\ 5\tfrac{4}{12} \\ \hline & & 4\tfrac{5}{12} \end{aligned}$$

Page 125

10. (4) 131.7 miles

```
  5 0.2
  1 3.7
+ 6 7.8
1 3 1.7
```

11. (3) $28.60

```
 $2 5.5 0        2 8.6 0
  1 9.9 0     3 )$8 5.8 0
+   4 0.4 0      6
 $8 5.8 0        2 5
                 2 4
                 1 8
                 1 8
                  0
                  0
```

12. (3) $251.31   25% = 0.25

```
 $1 1 9.5 0              $1 1 9.5 0
   × 0.2 5             −     2 9.8 8
   5 9 7 5 0             $8 9.6 2
 2 3 9 0 0
 $2 9.8 7 5 0 → $29.88
```

```
 $8 9.6 2        7% = 0.07
  7 9.5 0
  2 9.7 5        $2 3 4.8 7
+   3 6.0 0        × 0.0 7
 $2 3 4.8 7      $1 6.4 4 0 9 → $16.44
```

```
 $2 3 4.8 7
+    1 6.4 4
 $2 5 1.3 1
```

13. (3) 7 hr 30 min

7:30 a.m. to noon:

```
   12 hr            11 hr 60 min
−   7 hr 30 min      7 hr 30 min
                     4 hr 30 min
```

noon to 3:30 p.m. is 3 hr 30 min

```
  4 hr 30 min
+ 3 hr 30 min
  7 hr 60 min  =  8 hr
```

```
  8 hr             7 hr 60 min
−       30 min            30 min
                   7 hr 30 min
```

14. (2) 49 dinners

```
    3 0 2
  − 2 5 3
      4 9
```

Page 126

15. (5) $222

```
 $1 8       $1 5        $1 5 0
  × 4       × 1 0      +   7 2
 $7 2         0 0       $2 2 2
              1 5
            $1 5 0
```

16. (3) $1\frac{1}{2}$ lb

$$\frac{1}{2} \times 3 = \frac{1}{2} \times \frac{3}{1} = \frac{3}{2} = 1\frac{1}{2}$$

17. (1) $42.27

```
   $6 3.2 7
 − 2 1.0 0
   $4 2.2 7
```

18. (4) $262.53

$$\begin{array}{r} \$2\,9.3\,7 \\ +\ \ 1\,5.0\,0 \\ \hline \$4\,4.3\,7 \end{array} \qquad \begin{array}{r} \$2\,2\,5.7\,8 \\ -\ \ \ \ 4\,4.3\,7 \\ \hline \$1\,8\,1.4\,1 \end{array} \qquad \begin{array}{r} \$1\,8\,1.4\,1 \\ +\ \ \ \ 8\,1.1\,2 \\ \hline \$2\,6\,2.5\,3 \end{array}$$

19. (3) 720 ft

$$\begin{array}{r} 2\,5\,0 \\ 2\,5\,0 \\ 1\,1\,0 \\ +\ 1\,1\,0 \\ \hline 7\,2\,0 \end{array}$$

Page 127

20. (5) 108 tiles

$$\begin{array}{r} 1\,2 \\ \times\ \ 9 \\ \hline 1\,0\,8 \end{array}$$

21. (1) $12,050

$$\begin{array}{r} \$1\,5,1\,2\,5 \\ -\ \ \ \ 3,0\,7\,5 \\ \hline \$1\,2,0\,5\,0 \end{array}$$

22. (1) $100

$$\begin{array}{r} 5\,2 \\ \times\ 5 \\ \hline \$2\,6\,0 \end{array} \qquad \begin{array}{r} \$2\,6\,0 \\ -\ \ 1\,6\,0 \\ \hline \$1\,0\,0 \end{array}$$

23. (5) 8 times

$$3 \div \frac{3}{8} =$$

$$\frac{\overset{1}{\cancel{3}}}{1} \times \frac{8}{\cancel{3}} = 8$$

24. (4) $71.40

$$\begin{array}{r} \$5.9\,5 \\ \times\ 1\,2 \\ \hline 1\,1\,9\,0 \\ 5\,9\,5 \\ \hline \$7\,1.4\,0 \end{array}$$

Page 128

25. (1) 73%

$$\begin{array}{r} 1\,0\,0\% \\ -\ \ 2\,7\% \\ \hline 7\,3\% \end{array}$$

26. (1) 25 sq yd

$$3\overline{)1\,5} = 5 \qquad \begin{array}{r} 5 \\ \times\ 5 \\ \hline 2\,5 \end{array}$$

27. (5) 44,817 miles

$$\begin{array}{r} 3\,2,5\,5\,7 \\ +\ 1\,2,2\,6\,0 \\ \hline 4\,4,8\,1\,7 \end{array}$$

28. (2) 16 gallons

$$\begin{array}{r} 1\,6 \\ 1\,8\overline{)2\,8\,8} \\ 1\,8 \\ \hline 1\,0\,8 \\ 1\,0\,8 \end{array}$$

29. (3) 24 packages

$$100 \div 2\frac{1}{2} =$$

$$100 \div \frac{5}{2} =$$

$$\frac{\overset{20}{\cancel{100}}}{1} \times \frac{2}{\cancel{5}} = 40$$

$$\frac{\overset{8}{\cancel{40}}}{1} \times \frac{2}{\cancel{5}} = 16$$

$$\begin{array}{r} 4\,0 \\ -\ 1\,6 \\ \hline 2\,4 \end{array}$$

Page 129

30. (1) $19.97

$$\begin{array}{r} 1\,9.9\,7 \\ 4\overline{)\$7\,9.8\,8} \\ 4 \\ \hline 3\,9 \\ 3\,6 \\ \hline 3\,8 \\ 3\,6 \\ \hline 2\,8 \\ 2\,8 \end{array}$$

31. (2) 85 people $34\% = 0.34$

$$\begin{array}{r} 2\,5\,0 \\ \times\ 0.3\,4 \\ \hline 1\,0\,0\,0 \\ 7\,5\,0 \\ \hline 8\,5.0\,0 \end{array}$$

32. (2) 88 pounds

$$
\begin{array}{r}
1\ 2\ 5 \\
+\ \ \ 8\ 7 \\
\hline
2\ 1\ 2
\end{array}
\qquad
\begin{array}{r}
3\ 0\ 0 \\
-\ 2\ 1\ 2 \\
\hline
8\ 8
\end{array}
$$

33. (3) $\frac{1}{4}$ of the pizza

34. (5) $13,500

$$
\begin{array}{c}
\overset{4500}{\cancel{18000}} \\
\overline{1}
\end{array}
\times
\dfrac{1}{\underset{1}{\cancel{4}}}
= 4,500
\qquad
\begin{array}{r}
\$1\ 8,0\ 0\ 0 \\
-\ \ \ \ 4,5\ 0\ 0 \\
\hline
\$1\ 3,5\ 0\ 0
\end{array}
$$

Page 130

35. (4) $218.75

$$
\begin{array}{r}
3.5 \\
+\ 5.2\ 5 \\
\hline
8.7\ 5
\end{array}
\qquad
\begin{array}{r}
8.7\ 5 \\
\times\ \ \ 2\ 5 \\
\hline
4\ 3\ 7\ 5 \\
1\ 7\ 5\ 0 \\
\hline
\$2\ 1\ 8.7\ 5
\end{array}
$$

36. (4) $108.50

$30\% = 0.30$

$$
\begin{array}{r}
\$1\ 5\ 5 \\
\times\ 0.3\ 0 \\
\hline
0\ 0\ 0 \\
4\ 6\ 5 \\
\hline
\$4\ 6.5\ 0
\end{array}
\qquad
\begin{array}{r}
\$1\ 5\ 5.0\ 0 \\
-\ \ \ 4\ 6.5\ 0 \\
\hline
\$1\ 0\ 8.5\ 0
\end{array}
$$